Rock Trails

Snowdonia

Paul Gannon

Pesda Press LTD

www.pesdapress.com

Cover Photo: Tryfan from Y Garn,
Pierino Algieri (www.algieri-images.co.uk)

First published in Great Britain 2008 by Pesda Press
Unit 22, Galeri
Doc Victoria
Caernarfon
Gwynedd
LL55 1SQ

ISBN: 978-1-906095-04-8

Printed in Poland, produced by Polska Book.

To Tim and Clair

The summit of Snowdon at sunset.

Contents

Foreword

The mountains represent a living museum of geological history of unfathomable timescale. Their archives hint at a grand story, revealed in detail in the small print, which explains something of this spiralling rock we call earth.

My understanding of geology is sketchy in the extreme, but it's now reckoned that the earth itself is about 4,500 million years old. The rocks of northern Snowdonia were laid down, apparently, over 400 million years ago, so the Earth was already old when Snowdonia appeared. This story told in this book reaches back from the present day, to the Cambrian era which predates the rocks of Snowdon.

I wonder if, like me, you find it difficult to comprehend vast spans of time such as these? A number of years ago I took myself off into the seclusion of Torridon to contemplate the question of time and space. I found it easy enough to consider events of a hundred years, or even five hundred, but was lost trying to contemplate the ages of our mountains.

I remember stopping on a rocky platform on a hill called Baosbheinn and looking over and beyond the lonely waters of Loch na h-Oidhche. It was then that I realised for the first time that nearby Beinn an Eoin and neighbouring Beinn Dearg were made up of layer upon layer of rock, which were replicas of the strata that I was now climbing on Baosbheinn. I could see clearly, as my eye moved downhill, that the rocks were becoming older, from the relatively young sandstone peaks (now toothless, but once graced by quartzite caps), down through the aeons to darker, older slopes and the bedrock of ancient gneiss. Created over millions of years, over millions of years they were being worn down.

It is easy to consider mountains as timeless, but here was evidence of the steady progress of time. I may have lacked great insight into the changes brought about over two hundred and fifty million years, but I felt more at ease with the concept. I went home more aware of my own impermanence amid these hoary giants that dominate our landscape.

The only way to get to grips with the legacy of our mountains, is walk amongst the ancient rocks, to climb them, to touch them and to feel their texture and their grain. This book will guide you to the signs which tell the most ancient story of all.

Cameron McNeish

Introduction

The spectacular mountain scenery of Snowdonia, with its arrays of steep rocky hills, atmospheric deep valleys and sparkling lakes, is one of the scenic highlights of the British Isles. The rugged beauty of the landscape attracts millions of visitors to North Wales every year. And of them, as many as half a million slog up to the summit of Snowdon – Yr Wyddfa in Welsh – on one or other of half-a-dozen popular walking routes. The walkers are there joined by another 200,000 or so who take a more leisurely journey to the top, thanks to the Snowdon Mountain Railway. Many thousands more stay in the valley, and come just to soak up the stunning landscape that stretches before them.

Photo 0.1 | View towards Snowdon from Capel Curig.

This book is intended to help those who love Snowdonia's mountain scenery to understand how this haunting landscape came about. I have divided the book into two parts. The first narrates the story of colliding continents, volcanoes, mountain-building and glaciation in creating Snowdonia, explaining why volcanoes occurred, what rocks they created and how to interpret signs of mountain-building and glaciation on the ground. The second half describes several recommended walks, of differing levels of difficulty, but all with a wide variety of geological features to be seen and, most important, enjoying consistently fantastic views of the very best of Snowdonia's wonderful scenery.

Photo 0.2 | Snowdon's western face and Cwm Clogwyn peeking out over a winter cloud inversion.

I hope the reader will come to appreciate the interplay of volcanoes, glaciation, erosion and other influences on the landscape. The aim is to enable the reader to identify major and minor landscape features in Snowdonia and maybe elsewhere too. The landscape we see before us is the product of many different forces and factors. Identifying and unravelling these forces and factors on the ground is an endlessly fascinating pastime for the landscape lover.

I have concentrated on what you can see as you walk around the hills without the need to use a hand lens or other geological tool, pointing instead to conspicuous, easily seen features in rocks and the overall shape of the terrain in accounting for the present day landscape.

While geology is a fascinating subject, it is also a science, and relies on a complex scientific terminology. My aim has been to minimise the use of jargon and to make the processes that have determined the shape of the landscape comprehensible to the average reader. This has meant some simplification of the jargon and a pruning of the detail. All the same, we will, I'm afraid, have to deal with a minimal set of terms such as 'plate tectonics' and 'fissure-vents', 'magma' and 'intrusive' rocks, 'ice sheets' and 'moraines', and the like.

When I first use a piece of jargon I have put it in quote marks (for example, 'continental plate'). Many of these terms are defined in the Glossary, but I have also sometimes assumed that the meaning of a term is obvious from the context in which it appears. Occasionally I have used quote marks to identify a bit of everyday idiom, such as a 'blob' of magma.

The reader may well find it useful, while reading the book, to have open and to hand a copy of the OS 1:25,000 map (OL17) or a larger scale map of Snowdon (such as the OS 1:50,000 or the Harvey 1:40,000). This will assist in locating places mentioned as examples in the text (with help of the list, at the back of the book, of grid references of all local places named in the text). A map will also help to convey an idea of the present-day physical shape of a location or feature and its surrounds when it is discussed.

Photo 0.3 | View east from Snowdon's summit.

CHAPTER 1

A View over 700 Million Years of Snowdonia

A good place to start our look at the landscapes of Snowdonia is just outside the village of Llanberis, at the 'viewing point' (marked on Ordnance Survey maps) high above the Welsh National Slate Museum on an old slate waste tip.[1]

Looking right (north-westwards) it is possible, on a clear day, to see the Menai Strait and Anglesey (Ynys Môn) in the distance, beyond the low ground that frames the long, narrow glacial lake, Llyn Padarn, and the low hills on either side of it. These low hills are the northern-most limits of the Snowdon massif and of the Glyderau range and will be the starting point for our view of the landscapes of Snowdonia. Here we will look at the landscape, formed out of grits, sandstones and mudstones that were originally laid down, about half-a-billion years ago, as sediments under the seas of a continental shelf. These low hills, their lower wooded slopes and the shimmering lake combine to create a mountain scenery that is soft, enticing and beautiful (see photo 1.1).

Photo 1.1 | View from National Slate Museum over Llyn Padarn, towards Anglesey.

[1] Grid reference 591 604. Reached by walking up the public footpath that zigzags up through the slate waste from the strip of land separating the two glacial lakes, Llyn Padarn and Llyn Peris, or, to save the climb, from the parking place at Dinorwig (591 611) and walking a few hundred metres on the level along a public footpath.

Looking to the left (south-eastwards) up the Llanberis Pass, beyond another thin glacial lake, Llyn Peris, the scene is completely different. Here the scenery is intensely dramatic. A trough-like glacial gorge, deeply etched into tough volcanic rocks, dominates the view of the main mountain landscape of Snowdonia, with steep, sharply-angled mountain slopes rearing upwards on either side. This is rough, craggy beauty. No softness, but compellingly harsh wilderness. Here we will see how violent volcanic eruptions and the collision of 'tectonic plates' poured out material that formed hard rocks and how, much later, massively powerful glaciers carved sharp edges into those tough volcanic rocks (see photo 1.2).

Photo 1.2 | View along the Llanberis Pass over Llyn Peris, towards Pen y Pass.

But there's another unavoidable aspect to the landscape, especially from this viewing point, which stands atop a quarry waste tip. For here, the massive, now abandoned, Dinorwig slate quarry is above, below and all around you as soon as you turn away from the outward view (see photo 1.3). This is the landscape that humans have made. Despite the mountain scenery and its appearance of being a wilderness, Snowdonia is also an intensely human landscape. Nowhere is this point more forcefully made than in the midst of the immense quarry workings at the northern end of the Snowdon massif and the Glyderau ridge – but we will also see plenty of other, though often less conspicuous, traces of human influence on the landscape.

On Anglesey some of the very oldest rocks are around 700 million years old. Moving into the area of our focus, the low hills on the northern flanks of Llyn Padarn are nearly 600 million years old. The slate beds all around here were originally mudstones laid down about 500 million years ago. The volcanic rocks forming the crags further up the valley, towards the head

Photo 1.3 | View from
Dinorwig 'viewing point'
towards slate quarry.

of the Llanberis Pass, date from about 450 million years ago. Despite the enormously long time since these volcanic rocks were laid down, these are the 'youngest' rocks in our area.

The intervening 450 million years, since these final rocks were laid down, saw the building in the area of a massive mountain range – at least as high as the Alps, perhaps even as high as the Himalayas – which has, since then, been subject to erosion. So, roughly, we may say that it took about 250 million years to lay down the rock from which the mountains of Snowdonia and its surrounding region were built, and another 450 million years to turn those rocks into the shapes we see to day.

The earth itself is now thought to be about 4,500 million years old, so the 450 million year period since the rocks of the northern Snowdonia were laid down represents just 10% of the earth's total history. And the 250 million years it took to lay down those rocks is a mite over 5% of the earth's history. Thus, from our viewpoint on a slate waste tip at Dinorwig, we are looking at about 15% of the earth's actual time span. That is the time period in which our story unfolds.

It is of course extremely difficult for us to comprehend these sorts of time scales when, if we are lucky, we measure our own life spans in just a few score years. However, long-term geological processes can actually make sense when thought about as things that happen over millions of years. For example, sediments (eroded from higher land and washed down by rivers to be laid as, say, mud or sand and later compressed into 'sedimentary' rock) may be laid down at a rate of, say, one millimetre in ten years. Apparently this is not much. But it makes one centimetre over a hundred years, ten centimetres over a thousand years, a metre over ten thousand years, ten metres over a hundred thousand years and a hundred metres after one million years – though the processes of drying out, squeezing under pressure of accumulated weight and transformation into rock ('lithification') will reduce that thickness quite a bit.

If sediments are laid down continuously for millions of years, quite thick layers can thus be built up. The same also applies in reverse – millions of years of erosion and weathering, however minimal each year – can reduce massive mountains to little more than humps.

Some geological processes are slow, accumulative, all but imperceptible on a human timescale. But there is another aspect to geological processes. Individual events within a process can happen in a short space of time.

The tsunami which struck south Asia at the end of 2004, with dreadful consequences for so many people, is an example of a short, sharp and sudden geological process. In that particular case a sudden movement of the earth on the line of a tear or crack in the earth's structure, a 'fault' (or set of faults in a 'fault zone'). Despite its suddenness the earthquake, and the tsunami it generated, formed just one event in a much longer-term background process – movement on one of the boundaries between tectonic plates, which consist of a continental or oceanic crust and the uppermost layer of the earth's 'mantle', and which form the earth's surface. These independent 'plates' are moving relative to each other, propelled into collision by convection currents within the earth, and often causing volcanic activity.

This is the current view of geologists in the theory of 'plate tectonics'. Having taken many years to gain acceptance among geologists, the theory is now at the very core of our under-standing of the earth in general – and of how the mountains of Snowdonia were created.

We will enter the story sometime between 700 million to 600 million years ago, focussing on a section of the earth where there are two continents, Avalonia and Lauentia, separated by an ocean, the Iapetus (it may help to think of Avalonia as ancient western Europe, Laurentia as ancient North America and the Iapetus as the ancient Atlantic Ocean).

One small point is worth noting – continental crust usually extends under sea with a 'continental shelf' and a 'continental slope' down to where the plates actually meet. Most of the geological 'action' in North Wales took place in this boundary zone, sometimes under sea, sometimes above it, near the edge of its continental plate.

What will become North Wales is near the edge of Avalonia facing the Iapetus ocean in an area of ancient fault zones (the product of much earlier tectonic activity), faults which stretch deep into the earth's crust. These main fault zones ran from the north-east to the south-west, though with subsidiary faults roughly at right angles to this trend, running from north-west to south-east.

Volcanic activity about 600 million years ago, along the line of some of these faults, produced the rocks, almost white-looking, that form the low hills on either side of Llyn Padarn (see photo 1.4). The rocks are known as the 'Padarn Tuffs' and were laid down, in a deep trough between the fault zones, by extremely violent volcanic eruptions. These eruptions were unrelated to the main Snowdon volcanic eruptions which we will look at in later chapters and remind us that volcanic activity has been going on for many aeons ('tuff' is a name for a type of volcanic rock and which we will look at a bit more closely in those later chapters).

Photo 1.4 | Padarn Tuffs:
Craig yr Undeb – Union Rock
at the north-western end
of Llyn Padarn (so called
because the North Wales
Quarrymen's Union was
formed and met here).

The toughness of the Padarn Tuffs is evident from that fact that they have lasted so long, still standing as high points despite the recent ice ages and all the other events they have experienced since they were laid down. After all these years the Padarn Tuffs now produce a very poor soil, not even sufficient to support sheep grazing (the minerals having been leached away over the last 600 million years). Heather, gorse and bracken grow in profusion. The few paths are hard to find and easy to lose, dumping the walker in very rough ground, with hidden rocks that threaten to trip you up at every step (see photos 1.5, w10.3 and w10.4).

Yet these low heights – Cefn Du on the western side of the lake and Y Clegr on the eastern side – offer superb views of Snowdon and the Glyderau, of Llyn Padarn, of other ranges and of Ynys Môn (Anglesey), the Menai Strait and the sea. The hills are low enough to remain below cloud most of the time, even when the higher peaks are wreathed in mist, providing good views in most conditions. A walk around Llyn Padarn at low level is one of the easiest walks in the area, but walking around it on the higher ground either side can be quite challenging (see Walk 10).

After the volcanic eruptions that produced the Padarn Tuffs had died down, the area that would become central Snowdonia was for a long time below sea level. Sandstones, siltstones

Photo 1.5 | Y Clegr – outcrops of Padarn Tuffs (foreground), Snowdon massif (distant centre & right).

and 'conglomerates' (rocks containing pebbles of other rocks) were being laid down, forming layer upon layer of sedimentary rocks (it is the size of the sedimentary particles from which a rock is made up that determines whether the rock is called a mudstone, a siltstone, a sandstone, a grit or a conglomerate, from smaller particles to larger).

For many millions of years great thicknesses of 'mudstones' were laid down on top of one another – mudstones that would one day become world famous as the purple and blue-grey slates of North Wales, the process by which the mudstones became 'metamorphosed' into slate will be covered in chapter 6 (see photo 1.6).

As always is the case in geology, the situation is somewhat more complex than it initially sounds. Quite often rocks are more varied than their geological name implies. The layers of mudstones were interspersed with narrower layers of sandstones. Today the layers of mudstones and sandstones have been tilted, almost upright in places, and some of the sandstone layers have been exposed in the slate quarry faces. They are a light green in colour (see photo 1.7). One point to note regarding the identification of rock type is that a rock's colour is affected by 'weathering', the chemical breakdown of rock in the atmosphere (and by the growth of 'lichen' on the rock surface). Throughout this book when I refer to what a rock looks like I am describing its weathered and partially lichen-covered condition, as this is the state in which the hillwalker sees them. However this does not apply in those few odd circumstances where a 'fresh' rock face is exposed, such as seen in quarries. Both slate and sandstone weather to a fairly similar looking grey colour when not exposed in quarry faces.

After the mudstones, came bands of tough sandstones and grits, known as the Bronll-wyd Grits. These grits were followed by the Marchlyn Flags (softer sandstones and siltstones),

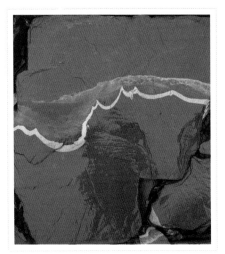

Photo 1.6 (top) | Llanberis purple slate.

Photo 1.7 (right) | Light green sandstone beds within the Llanberis slate formation.

and then by more tough sandstones and conglomerates, known as the Carnedd y Filiast Grits (similar grits form the area to the south of Snowdon, the mountains around Rhinog Fawr and Rhinog Fach, another excellent area for walking).

The 'succession' of these rocks can be seen in the relief of the northern Glyderau hills. The shallow bwlch (col) between Elidir Fach and Elidir Fawr represents the band of softer siltstones sandwiched between the tougher bands of grits. Exactly the same effect is mirrored on the other arm of the ridge, between 'spot height 721' and the summit of Carnedd y Filiast. The relationship between the toughness of the rock and the shape of the landscape is easy to see on this side of the Llanberis valley (see photo 1.8, diagram 1.1 and photo 1.9) – but the succession of rocks is not so clear on the south-western side, as in some places the rocks have been turned upside down and pushed out of place during the later mountain-building forces (see chapter 6).

The walk round the horseshoe above Marchlyn Mawr, via Carnedd y Filiast, Mynydd Perfedd, Bwlch y Marchlyn and Elidir Fawr is one of the best walks in northern Snowdonia, providing

Viewed from eastern end of summit ridge, Elidir Fawr

Diagram 1.1 + Photo 1.8 | Carnedd y Filiast and 'spot height 721' – in this and photo 1.9 the relationship between height and rock type is well illustrated. Elidir Fawr and Carnedd y Filiast are made up of tough grits; while the bwlch (or col) to the left of each summit is made up of softer siltstones, and the slight rise to the left of each of these lower points is also formed of tough grits (foreground shows almost vertical beds of grits on the summit ridge on Elidir Fawr).

Photo 1.9 | Elidir Fawr and Elidir Fach (left distance).

fantastic views of the scenery and of a superb range of geological features (see Walk 6).

Going clockwise, the transition from the Marchlyn Flags to the Carnedd y Filiast Grits is particularly easy to spot, as you climb above the shallow bwlch mentioned above, on the steep final part of the ascent to the summit of Carnedd y Filiast. The softer flags, which crumble into small pieces of slate on the track, give way to prominent grey outcrops of grits. These form quite big blocks and offer the opportunity for scrambling as well as for studying the variety of rock types within the 'formation' (the Carnedd y Filiast Grits are one formation, the Marchlyn Flags another formation, and so on).

The Carnedd y Filiast Grits also form one of the most impressive geological sights in central Snowdonia. Just east of the summit of Carnedd y Filiast, at the edge of the ridge, this amazing geological feature can be viewed from the edge looking over Cwm Graianog, from either side on the stonewall that transects the summit plateau (see photo 1.10).

Sedimentary rocks may display a feature known as 'bedding'. This occurs when the process of sedimentation is interrupted, before more sediments are laid down on top – for example in tidal conditions or between disturbances caused by earthquakes. Each interruption produces a distinct 'bed' or 'bedding plane'. Sometimes ripples created by waves (as seen on a sandy beach) are preserved in the bedding plane, then covered over as more layers are built up and

Photo 1.10 | Carnedd y Filiast Grits – rippled bedding spectacularly exposed in Cwm Graianog.

then slowly hardened into rock ('lithification'). Now, as the rocks are eroded away, the old bedding planes may be exposed and it is possible to see these fossilized ripples created several hundred million years ago (though some sedimentary rocks do not display bedding at all, others only now and again, and where bedding does occur each bed may vary in thickness).

All the beds of sedimentary rocks we've looked at were originally laid down horizontally, but here you can see how later mountain-building forces have tilted the beds to quite a steep angle (chapter 6). Later still, the glacier that developed in Cwm Graianog (chapter 8) dug back into the rock, undermining it and leading to its collapse. Tension, caused by gravity, pulled the rocks apart along the weakness of old bedding planes. Great masses of rock slid down into the cwm. Looking down you can see some of the rocks that collapsed and were piled up into moraines. But most impressive of all, you can also see the bedding planes in the rock face just a few feet below you and stretching down into the cwm. The quite sizeable ripples were left in the beds by water currents at the time the rocks were laid down (with ripples up to 15cm high and with a variable 'wavelength' of between 30cm and 1.5 metres). See photo 1.11.

The tilt of the beds is also evident on the summit ridge of Elidir Fawr. The summit is a magnificent viewpoint and should not be missed by the hillwalker in Snowdonia. The views are spectacular and provide an excellent overview of the mountains we are going to look at in this book and also of the mountain ranges beyond.

Elidir Fawr is one of the 14 Welsh peaks that exceed the height of 3,000 feet. It is the only one of the 14 that is not made up of predominantly volcanic material, but is the product of the tough sedimentary rocks, the Carnedd y Filiast Grits. It also stands somewhat distant

Photo 1.11 (top) |
Carnedd y Filiast Grit: rippled bedding in close up (in Cwm Dwythwch) – the 'wavelength' of the ripples is between 0.30m and 1.5m indicating a powerful current.

Photo 1.12 (middle) |
Carnedd y Filiast Grit: bedding – note varying thickness of beds, with thicker beds indicating stabler conditions (near Nant Peris; height of field of view 1m).

Photo 1.13 (bottom) |
Carnedd y Filiast Grits: quartz pebbles – the pebbles range in size from small peas to cashew nuts (Cwm Graianog).

from all the other Welsh 3,000 foot peaks, a serrated ridge from one angle, a sharp pyramid from another. According to some, its real name is Carnedd Elidir – the cairn of Elidir, probably an ancient Briton of legend.

The walk along the top of the summit ridge of Elidir Fawr, as well as providing some more of those magnificent views, also allows you to observe closely the different beds of the Carnedd y Filiast Grits, including a very distinctive conglomerate with lumps of rounded quartz cemented together in a 'matrix' of other material (see photos 1.12 and 1.13). I found a fossil along the underside of some of these beds one day on the summit ridge, very similar to other fossils I had previously found in an outcrop of these same grits down in the Llanberis Pass (see photo 1.14).

The Carnedd y Filiast Grits are the final rocks in the area laid down during what is known as the 'Cambrian era'. Geologists divide the past into a number of eras (see diagram 1.3). Each era represents a significant development in the 'fossil record'. The appearance of the same fossils in rocks in different areas allows geologists to work out what rocks were laid down in what order. The Cambrian era is when the number, variety and complexity of marine animals increased dramatically. A form of animal known as a 'trilobite' was especially common in our area and the fossils I found were examples of what is known as 'trace' fossils, which means the fossil is not the animal itself, but an impression or trace left by it in soft sand. The photograph shows the trace left in the sand by the legs of a resting trilobite.

This might not seem so exciting as finding the remains of the beast itself, but trace fossils are not in the least to be seen as second-class citizens. Usually only the hard, skeletal parts of animals are preserved in fossils, with no real evidence of the softer body parts. So, a trace fossil of the trilobite's resting limbs (if that interpretation is correct) gives some scarce information about these animals that is not normally to be gleaned from fossil finds.

It is possible to find fossils in the mountains throughout our area – including the summit of Snowdon – but they are comparatively rare and it takes a lot of looking or luck to find any, so I will not complicate the story by going into details of different fossil types. But, keep your eyes open and you never know what you will see.

The Cambrian era roughly covers the period from about 543 million to 490 million years ago. All time before the Cambrian is lumped together in the 'Precambrian'. After the Cambrian, comes another change in the fossil record and a new era, known as the 'Ordovician', covering the period from about 490 million to 430 million years ago. As usual with geology, there is

Photo 1.14 | Carnedd y Filiast Grit: Cruziana fossil (about 5cm long). This is a 'trace' fossil, the impression left by the legs of a 'trilobite' at rest. I have also found this type of fossil near Nant Peris and on the summit ridge of Elidir Fawr.

the inevitable complexity as geologists frequently revise the allocation of rocks to the different era as their knowledge increases.

For example, up until the mid-1980s the Padarn Tuffs were considered as Precambrian rocks, but they have now been re-assigned to the Cambrian era itself – although you may still find them referred to as Precambrian in some books.

All the rocks in our area were laid down in either the Cambrian or the Ordovician eras, so in general we need not bother overmuch about the names and dates of the other eras (see diagram 1.2), except for the eras immediately after the Ordovician, known as the Silurian and the Devonian, for it was during these two eras that the rocks of Snowdonia were pushed upwards into a mountain range.

After the last Cambrian rocks (the Carnedd y Filiast Grits) were laid down, the area was elevated above sea level for many millions of years, so no new rocks were created during that time in present-day North Wales. Thus there is, in our area, a big gap in the rock record, with no rocks from the early- or mid-Ordovician era. It was only towards the end of the Ordovician era that the area was once again below sea level and once again more sedimentary rocks were laid down.

These Ordovician sedimentary rocks make up some of the shapely summits of the hills framing Llanberis: Moel Eilio, the

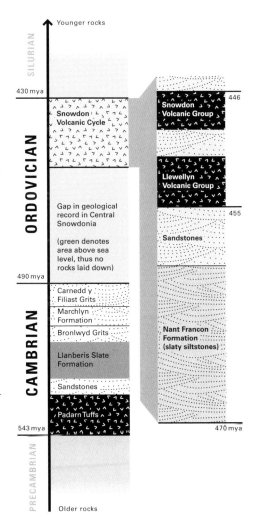

Diagram 1.2 | Geological 'time column' for central Snowdonia, 570 million to 438 million years ago. Green area denotes land above sea level (no sediment laid down).

23

ridge to its south, Moel Cynghorion and the northern end of the Llanberis Ridge (see photo 1.15). They are the product of the softer shales and siltstones of the 'Nant Ffrancon beds' as these sedimentary rocks are called. Like many of the mountains in the area, Moel Eilio and Moel Cynghorion show two distinct faces, with rounded grassy slopes facing south-west and steep craggy ones facing north-east. This is a product of how the rocks responded to glacial scouring in the much later Ice Age and need not concern us here, except to note the rounded, grassy aspect of the hills (moel/foel = 'smooth, rounded or treeless hill'). These hills provide comparatively easy mountain walking, though they should not be underestimated.

Photo 1.15 | From left to right: Moel Cynghorion, Foel Goch and Moel Eilio (middle distance) from above Dinorwig quarry.

The walk along the ridge from Moel Eilio towards Moel Cynghorion offers some excellent views towards Snowdon – for the best views tackle the walk in a counter-clockwise direction, aiming first for Moel Eilio, climbing up either the north or north-eastern ridge, and then heading south along the main ridge (see photo 1.16). Continuing in the same direction over Moel Cynghorion presents unrivalled views into the rocky chaos of nature's own quarry, the glacial rockfest of Cwm du'r Arddu, on Snowdon's northern flank.

Photo 1.16 | View along Moel Eilio Ridge to Snowdon. All the hills in front of Snowdon are made up of sedimentary rocks of the Ordovician era.

On the other side of the Llanberis Pass, on the northern Glyderau Ridge, the Ordovician sedimentary rocks form Foel Goch, the low summit between Elidir Fawr and Y Garn (and not to be confused with the Foel Goch on the Moel Eilio Ridge). Although a low summit, or perhaps because of it, this Foel Goch is an excellent viewpoint with a 360 degree panorama of the surrounding, higher mountain summits and should not be by-passed if you are walking this part of the Glyderau Ridge (see photo 1.17)

The rocks you see underfoot on these hills are dark blue/grey and slate-like. However, in general, they do not produce 'workable' (i.e. economically extractable and saleable) slate as they don't split as cleanly as good quality slate. The Cambrian-era Llanberis Slate beds produced slate that did split cleanly and very thinly – ideal for uses such as roofing tiles and writing slates. However, you can stumble across small trial workings, and will need to circumnavigate some reasonably big quarries, in odd places all over the Snowdon massif in particular (such as opposite Nant Peris, in Cwm Llan and above Rhyd Ddu).

In this chapter we have moved from a vague basement rock platform on Anglesey, dating from before 700 million years ago, jumping rapidly to 540 million years ago in our area at the start of the Cambrian era, to near the end of the Ordovician era, a time period of some

Photo 1.17 | Foel Goch (top right) in the Glyderau – a comparatively low hill, but an excellent viewpoint, made up of sedimentary rocks of the Ordovician era. Tryfan in the centre distance.

200 million years. On our journey we have wandered over a substantial thickness of rocks of different types, mainly sedimentary, visible on either side of the Llanberis Pass and forming the foothills to the bigger, starker mountains to the south. Now it's time to change our focus and switch from the unfathomable aeons of sedimentation to the fast forward motion of a few short millions of years of volcanic activity.

CHAPTER 2

Crashing Plates and Mighty Volcanoes

Many people who climb up Snowdon wonder about the origin of its rocks. They may well have some notion that it was once a volcano, an impression easily reinforced by the pointed shape of its summit as seen from many angles, giving it the appearance of the classic cone-shaped volcano. The truth is that Snowdon is volcanic, but it wasn't a volcano as such.

Most of the volcanic eruptions which created Snowdonia's rocks occurred below sea level. They took place, in the main, through 'fissure-vents' along the lines of ancient faults that had been re-activated by forces created by the collision of 'tectonic plates', rather than through a single cone volcano.

In this chapter we will look at the circumstances in which the eruptions that created Snowdonia occurred and at some general aspects of the tectonic 'plate collision' before moving on, in the next two chapters, to look at the specific sites of volcanic activity in our area and the rocks that were created.

As mentioned in the last chapter, the earth's lithosphere is made up of independent 'tectonic plates' of which there are two types: 'oceanic plates' and 'continental plates'. The oceanic plate under the Iapetus Ocean reached its maximum width of about 5,000 kilometres (approximately 3,000 miles) about 500 million years ago, after which the convection currents working below the surface of the earth started pushing the two continental plates of Avalonia (our area) and Laurentia (the other side of the Iapetus Ocean) towards each other. The result of this was that the Iapetus oceanic plate was squeezed between the two continental plates and the ocean began to get narrower (see map 2.1).

Continental plates are made up of less dense material than ocean plates, so when the two different types of plate collide, the more buoyant continental plate tends to rise up above the oceanic plate. The oceanic plate is pushed down below the crust of the earth into the 'mantle', it is 'subducted' in geologists' jargon (see diagram 2.1).

This downward motion of the oceanic plate is the primary factor causing volcanic eruptions on a colliding boundary between oceanic and continental plates. It was volcanic activity generated by the Iapetus ocean plate being pushed down, or subducted, under the Avalonian continental plate that led, towards the end of the Ordovician era some 430

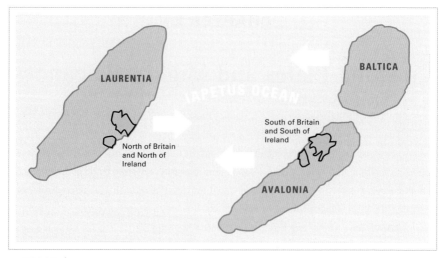

Map 2.1 | Avalonia, Iapetus Ocean, Laurentia.

million years ago, to the rocks of present day Snowdon being expelled from deep within the earth.

The volcanic eruptions in North Wales were only part of a much wider set of volcanic activity on the edge of the Avalonian continental plate. The eruptions in Snowdonia were the last to occur in a cycle of eruptions during the Ordovician era, all along the colliding plate boundary and which also affected other parts of Wales, the Lake District and southern Ireland (see map 2.2).

The process starts with the subduction of the oceanic plate under the continental plate as the two collided. When the subducting lump of oceanic plate starts to descend it stays solid for some distance as it plunges into the 'mantle' below the earth's lithosphere. This leaves a wedge of the underlying mantle caught between the still solid bit of the subducting oceanic plate below and the continental plate above.

Water is released from the oceanic plate, as it subducts, into the wedge area. The presence of water has the effect of lowering the temperature needed to melt the mantle rocks – so rocks in the wedge area of mantle become molten 'magma'. The molten magma then begins to move upwards, due to its lighter density relative to overlying rocks, deforming the shape of the overlying land. Some of the magma reaches the surface through faults and weaknesses in the form of volcanic eruptions.

In a later part of the subduction cycle more magma is created further inland under the continental plate. This is due to the plate flexing and thinning in reaction to the stresses created by subduction, resulting in a basin, below sea level, where more volcanic eruptions occur – this was the part of the cycle during which present-day Snowdonia was created.

The whole volcanic cycle took many millions of years to take place, with many millions between each phase of eruptions. Each phase, such as those in North Wales, would then last for a few hundred thousand years, with the phase consisting of many different individual eruptions lasting a few hours, days or weeks, perhaps spread over a few thousand years.

All these eruptions occurred around the old fault systems, which provided weak points around which the earth could move and adjust to the pressure of the rising magma and to earthquakes caused by the subducting plate scraping against the undersurface of the continental plate. The faults also provided 'conduits' through which the magma could reach the surface as eruptions.

There are many different types of volcanic eruption (depending mainly on the chemical composition of the molten magma), but we can divide them roughly into two main types: eruptions which produce flows of lava; and 'pyroclastic' eruptions, where solid or molten fragments of magma and surrounding rock, as well as hot gases, are ejected in extremely violent explosions in various forms such as clouds of ash or incandescent flows of mate-

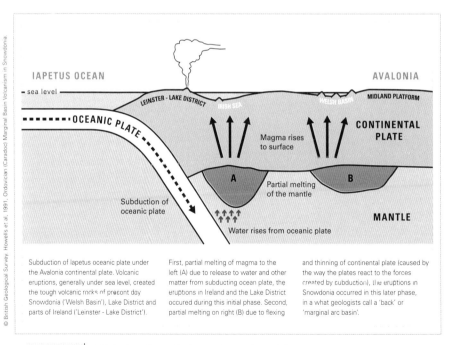

Subduction of Iapetus oceanic plate under the Avalonia continental plate. Volcanic eruptions, generally under sea level, created the tough volcanic rocks of present day Snowdonia ('Welsh Basin'), Lake District and parts of Ireland ('Leinster - Lake District').

First, partial melting of magma to the left (A) due to release to water and other matter from subducting ocean plate, the eruptions in Ireland and the Lake District occured during this initial phase. Second, partial melting on right (B) due to flexing

and thinning of continental plate (caused by the way the plates react to the forces created by subduction), the eruptions in Snowdonia occurred in this later phase, in a what geologists call a 'back' or 'marginal arc basin'.

Diagram 2.1 | Subduction of oceanic plate under continental plate.

rial. The ancient Padarn Tuffs, met in the previous chapter, were the product of such violent pyroclastic eruptions, and, as we shall see in the next two chapters, pyroclastic eruptions were central to producing the rocks of the present-day mountains of Snowdonia.

So, having set the scene, it is now time to look at where evidence of volcanic activity, dating from 430 million years ago, can be seen on the ground today in Snowdonia.

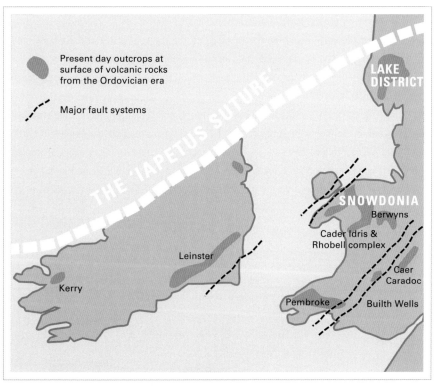

Map 2.2 | Ordovician volcanic rock, general map Wales and Ireland.

CHAPTER 3

The Pitts Head Tuffs

As we saw in the previous chapter, the episode of volcanic activities in the central Snowdonia area was just one phase in a series of volcanic episodes as the Iapetus ocean plate was subducted under the Avalonian continental plate and which affected other parts of Wales, the Lake District and parts of Ireland. Each episode of volcanic activity was the result of a massive 'blob' of molten magma being created below the earth's crust and which then forced its way upwards, causing the shape of the overlying rocks to be distorted. Ancient fault systems, reactivated by the plate movements, provided a system of 'plumbing conduits' for the magma to rise towards the surface.

In this chapter and the next, we will look at the central Snowdonia volcanic eruptions in a bit more detail, dividing the overall cycle into a number of different phases, each of which produced a varied range of rocks, but with several types which are relatively easy to identify on the ground even today, 430 million years after they were erupted from molten magma. Two great 'eruptive cycles' in Snowdonia occurred over a period of about 3.5 million years, with periods of intense volcanic activity separated by longer, quieter periods.

The first major episode of volcanic activity in northern Wales, what geologists call the '1st Eruptive Cycle', affected in the main the area of the present day Carneddau range, though also leaving significant traces in the rocks of parts of the Glyderau Ridge. These volcanic rocks make up the highest summits of the Carneddau – Carnedd Dafydd, Carnedd Llewelyn and the peaks further north. This episode produced the 'Llewelyn Volcanic Group'. A short account of the 1st Eruptive Cycle and the Llewelyn Volcanic Group is included in Walk 5, so we will jump over it here and will begin with the 2nd Eruptive Cycle, which produced the rocks of the Snowdon Volcanic Group in central Snowdonia.

The first event in the 2nd Eruptive Cycle was the eruption of material that toughened into the formation of rocks known as the Pitts Head Tuff (PHT). These were extremely violent 'pyroclastic' eruptions. Molten fragments of magma, solidified pumice from previous eruptions and now ripped away in the explosive eruption, and hot gases were blasted out sideways at speeds of several hundred kilometres per hour in a glowing, incandescent cloud of matter and gas.

Pitts Head is a farm near Llwyd Mawr, west of Moel Hebog, which has given its name to this formation of tuffs as this was the centre of the eruptions. The PHT eruptions occurred on the line of the one of the deep-seated ancient fault zones, the Moel Hebog fault zone.

The PHT eruptions occurred in two phases. The first set of eruptions took place around a network of faults and fissure-vents. As the magma was expelled by the eruption the rocks at the centre of the network of faults collapsed into a circular feature known as a 'caldera', probably below sea level (see diagram 5.1). A vast volume of erupted material was retained within the caldera laying the rocks, up to 700 metres thick, that are today exposed in the hills of the western Nantlle Ridge (Craig Cwm Silyn and Mynydd Graig Goch).

The second set of eruptions resulted in an 'outflow' of pyroclastic matter and gas to the east. This nowadays crops out in various places all around central Snowdonia. It can be found around the flanks of Moel Hebog; to the south-west of the Aberglaslyn gorge; in two strings which cross the Gwyrfai valley south of the village of Rhyd Ddu and up to Cwm Clogwyn on Snowdon's western flank; in a long string from the ridge above Llyn du'r Arddu, across the Llanberis Pass to the summit of Y Garn in the Glyderau and beyond to Pen yr Ole Wen in the Carneddau; and finally another outcrop starts in the Llanberis Pass at Pont y Gromlech (see photo 3.1), disappears on the north-eastern flanks of the Pass to reappear a bit higher up the southern ridge of Glyder Fawr (easily reached from Pen y Pass) and then running between Glyder Fawr and Glyder Fach, past Llyn Bochlwyd below Tryfan and eventually joining up with the previously described string at the foot of Pen yr Ole Wen.

Photo 3.1 (left)
An outcrop of the Pitts Head Tuff (near Pont y Gromlech in the Llanberis Pass).

Diagram 3.1 (right)
Ash flow eruption.

These 'strings' are the present day surface outcrops of the PHT. They actually link up under the ground as a single, wider layer of volcanic material, folded into a 'syncline' or dip by later mountain-building forces (see chapter 6), so only the edges crop out today as long, narrow exposures of rock. All this material was produced by the 'outflow' eruption of the PHT volcanic centre. The eruption itself took place above sea level, and initially flowed across the land for about 10 to 15 kilometres before meeting the sea where it surged on for between 7 and 10 kilometres more. The outflow tuffs are up to 70 metres thick in places (see diagram 3.1).

Fortunately, the PHT is one of the most easily identifiable of all the volcanic rocks in central Snowdonia, the result of the explosive eruption which produced it. The PHT is the product of a 'pyroclastic surge', an extremely violent form of sideways flow. This type of surge is known to geologists by various names: 'ignimbrite' or 'welded tuff' (unfortunately these names are used inconsistently – see under 'tuffs' in the Glossary).

During subduction of the oceanic plate (caused by the collision between oceanic and continental plates) water and gases become mixed up with the molten magma. These add considerable violence to the explosive mix. Because the water and gases are held within the magma under great pressure they are expelled with great fury, in glowing clouds of steam, gas and mixed minerals, when they are finally released from high confinement pressures to low atmospheric ones – rather as carbonated drinks bubble over when the confining bottle top is first released.

All this outblast – of hot gases and liquids, accompanied by lumps of rock from the surrounding area and dollops of molten magma – is expelled at the same time, in a short

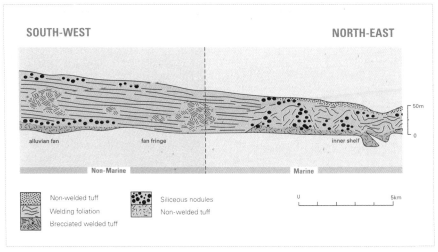

© British Geological Survey. Howells et al, 1991, Ordovician (Caradoc) Marginal Basin Volcanism in Snowdonia.

dramatic splurge. The resulting mix of burning gas and matter surges at enormous speed out in the ignimbrite flow, incinerating whatever stands in its path.

It was this mix of material and its intense heat that gave rise to one of the more easily identified rocks of the PHT – 'welded tuffs' in the geologists' jargon. The rocks blown away from the volcano in the ignimbrite eruption are partly made up of 'pumice' a glassy, light material produced by cooling magma from previous eruptions and intrusions.

The lumps of pumice become flattened by the heat and weight of the ignimbrite flow as it settles, and they become fully welded into the matrix of other smaller lumps and ashes of the flow. It is this flattening and 'welding' which gives welded tuffs their fairly recognisable appearance. The characteristic 'foliation' looks a bit like bedding in sedimentary rock (to add further confusion it also looks somewhat like a feature known as 'flow-banding' in some volcanic rock which we will meet in the next chapter). But once identified is fairly easy to distinguish in the case of the PHT (see photo 3.2).

As is so often the case with rocks generally, the PHT has a variety of forms, of which the welded tuff is only one (see diagram 3.1). The pyroclastic surge produced different effects at different points, with some non-welded tuffs, some partially welded tuffs, patches of broken (or 'brecciated') welded tuff, and also patches of 'siliceous nodules'. These nodules are another of the features that help identify outcrops as PHT (although it is important to appreciate that

Photo 3.2 | Pitts Head Tuff: a 'welded tuff' (Llanberis Ridge) – lumps of pumice blown away in the eruption are then carried along in a flow of incandescent ash, gas and magma, are heated and then crushed and 'welded' into the fabric of volcanic ash. Photo 10cm across.

Photo 3.3 (top)
Pitts Head Tuff:
'siliceous nodules'
(near Pont y Gromlech)
– the nodules in this
outcrop are the size of
eggs, but range from
pea-size to cannonball-
size in different outcrops
of the PHT, or can be
elongated to the shape
of a stubby cigar.

Photo 3.4 (bottom)
Pitts Head Tuff:
siliceous nodules
(near Pont y Gromlech).
Photo approximately
80cm across.

they are not exclusive to the PHT). The nodules range in size from marbles (just below the summit cairn on Y Garn, on the southern ridge of Glyder Fawr and in the outcrops at Dinas Gromlech in the Llanberis Pass) to the size of cannonballs (below the summit of Moel Hebog), and they can be roughly round-shaped or slightly elongated – like a short, stubby cigar (see photos 3.3, 3.4 and 3.5).

The PHT looks whiter than most rock outcrops, again aiding identification, especially if you can find welded tuffs and siliceous nodules too – but care needs to be taken as nodules can, for example, be seen in other volcanic rocks, for example, on the north ridge of Tryfan. But the combination of welded tuffs, nodules and whitish rocks means that it is relatively easy to identify PHT if you know that it outcrops in the area. The PHT is a particularly hard rock, often forming high points such as Y Garn in the Glyderau or the crags used by trainee climbers next to Pont y Gromlech in the floor of the Llanberis Pass where the road bridge crosses the river (see photo 3.1).

There are many creamy-white siliceous nodules littering the slopes just below the summit of Y Garn on the southern side as you ascend from Twll Du and Llyn y Cwn. The nodules must be harder even than the surrounding rock, for it has disappeared, leaving the nodules behind on the ground. You can also see outcrops of such nodules on the Glyder Fach walk (see recommended walks).

From whichever direction you ascend Y Garn, you will cross a number of geological boundaries and rock types, some volcanic and some sedimentary. Yet the very top of the present mountain is formed by the Pitts Head Tuffs that had flowed across land and then into the sea, fully welding some of the layers, partially welding others and also creating siliceous nodules. All this happened in an unimaginably violent explosion of burning ash and pumice. It seems hard to imagine as you enjoy the stunning panorama ranged around you from the pointed summit of Y Garn. But this is how the Pitts Head Tuff of central Snowdonia was born, in eruptions that were the precursors of some even more substantial explosions at the centre of the 2nd Eruptive Cycle.

Photo 3.5 | Pitts Head Tuff: siliceous nodules (side view). Photo approximately 1m across.

CHAPTER 4

The Snowdon Caldera Collapse

Following the eruptions which produced the Pitts Head Tuff there was a quiet period, with sedimentary rocks being laid down in places, deposited on top of the material emitted by the Pitts Head eruptions. But the effects of the collision of the Iapetus oceanic plate with the Avalonia continental plate continued to be worked through. In central Snowdonia it was a matter of the calm before the storm. A cycle of further eruptions started around the fault systems of central Snowdonia, eventually reached a climax, pouring out millions of cubic metres of volcanic matter, which today forms many of Snowdonia's scenic gems.

The first event in the new eruptive cycle was a series of lava eruptions, especially in the present day areas of the south-eastern limb of Cwm Idwal syncline, the Llanberis Pass on the northern side of the Snowdon massif, and in the western wall of Cwm Tregalan on Snowdon's southern side. A sheet of this basalt lava, some 18 metres thick, outcrops in Llanberis Pass.

Photo 4.1 Yr Arddu: view to Snowdon. The eruptions along the Yr Arddu fault initiated the main eruptive phase of the Snowdon Volcanic Group – the white-weathered rocks are further examples of welded tuffs.

These initial lava flows in central Snowdonia occurred at vents along two of the major fault lines – the 'Hebog-Idwal Fault Zone' and the 'Beddgelert Fault Zone'. Shortly after, a pyroclastic eruption occurred in the south-east corner of the network of faults in the area, near the area of present-day Yr Arddu (just west of the popular summit of Cnicht), along the 'Yr Arddu Fault Zone' (see photo 4.1). These were 'pyroclastic' eruptions, of 'rhyolitic' material and gases, which when deposited and hardened into rock, created rock types known as welded tuffs (see chapter 3) and 'breccias' (rock containing lumps of other rocks ripped up from surrounding rock during the volcanic eruption and solidified lumps of molten magma).

It's worth looking briefly at the differences between 'basaltic' and 'rhyolitic' volcanic rocks as they have influences on the type of rock and the landscape. Basaltic rocks are much more common around the world than rhyolitic ones, but the Snowdonia area is rich in the comparatively rare rhyolitic rocks.

Basaltic rocks (including sub-categories 'basalt lava', 'dolerite' and 'gabbro') are generally (but not always) dark in colour and, globally, are the most common types of volcanic or 'igneous' rock. While basalts are in general dark, rhyolites are in general lighter in colour (this 'lighter/darker' label applies to the weathered state of these rocks, not what they look like when freshly exposed to the atmosphere). We saw in the last chapter that the Pitts Head Tuffs are light-coloured – they too are rhyolitic rocks (as are the much more ancient Padarn Tuffs encountered in chapter 1).

The magma type depends on its chemical composition at any particular time – so that the blob of magma produced by subduction processes may be basaltic at one stage and rhyolitic later on depending on chemical processes within the magma. Basaltic magma is not very viscous and flows easily to produce widespread lavas. Rhyolitic magma, on the other hand, is extremely viscous and does not flow easily, thus it makes poor lavas. Instead the magma tends to congeal, thicken and cool in the 'vents' or faults, through which it is rising, before reaching the surface. This blocks the vent(s), contributes to the build up of explosive forces lower down in the volcanic 'plumbing' system and to eventual sudden and violent pyroclastic eruptions of fragments and gases. These highly explosive eruptions were common in the Snowdon eruptive cycle.

Today rhyolitic rocks dominate the scenery of our area – especially the bulk of the Snowdon massif, including Garnedd Ugain (Crib y Ddysgl), as well as the knife-edge ridge of Grib Goch and the twin peaks of Lliwedd on the far side of the Snowdon horseshoe, as well as many of the other peaks including Glyder Fawr, Glyder Fach and Tryfan.

The first pyroclastic eruptions, as mentioned above, occurred in the south-east of the area on the Yr Arddu Fault Zone (see map 4.1), creating the rocks (welded tuffs and breccias) that today form the low summit of Yr Arddu (just west of the popular peak of Cnicht – see photo 4.1). Then some more pyroclastic eruptions took place, not far from the Yr Arddu eruptions, along the line of the Beddgelert Fault Zone. The vent for the first of these eruptions was somewhere to the north-west of present-day Moel y Dyniewyd (near Beddgelert) and produced thin layers of welded tuffs on the southern flanks of Snowdon (below Yr Aran – see Walk 9) and around Moel y Dyniewyd.

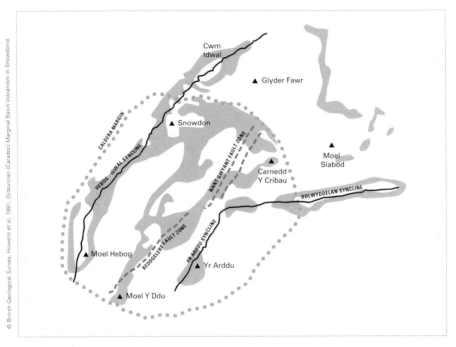

Map 4.1 | Yr Arddu and Lower Rhyolitic Tuffs (LRT) – present day outcrops and Snowdon caldera limits.

As the series of eruptions continued – probably lasting for at least many months – the centre of activity started to migrate to the north-east, up to the Nant Gwynant Fault Zone and to the northern end of the Hebog-Idwal Fault Zone, around present day Snowdon and the Llanberis Pass, and around Carnedd y Cribau. It was in this arc that enormous amounts of material were erupted, causing collapse of the dome of land pushed up by the rising magma and its collapse into a 'caldera', or a roughly circular area of sunken ground around, largely bounded by the old lines of faults marking the Snowdon fault zones (see diagram 4.1).

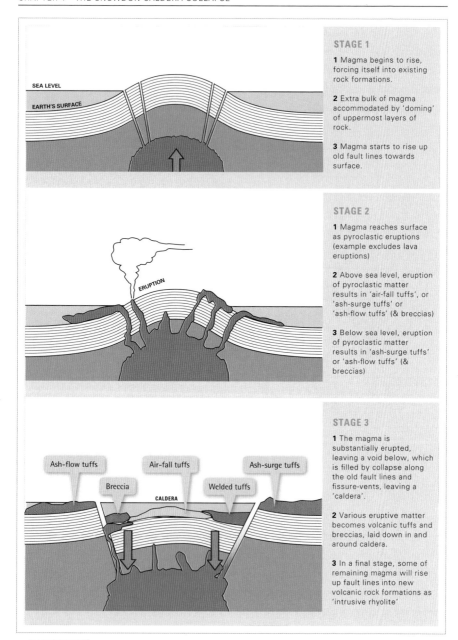

Diagram 4.1 | Caldera creation and types of pyroclastic eruption.

Perhaps as much as 60 million cubic metres of material was erupted. Much of the erupted material was contained within the collapsed caldera, but there was an 'outflow' of material to present-day Cwm Idwal (laying the rocks that today form the famous climbing area of the 'Idwal Slabs') and traces of eruptive material from this mega-eruption can be found running north almost as far as Conwy and east towards Dolwyddelan.

The collapsed caldera was roughly 10-12 kilometres in diameter, though somewhat elongated along the now familiar NE-SW trend of the major fault zones. The depth of the collapse was greatest in the northern area, where there was also the greatest intensity of eruptions – thus accounting for the considerable thicknesses of these rocks around Snowdon, Y Lliwedd, the Llanberis Pass and on Carnedd-y-Cribau.

The rocks produced by these pyrolastic eruptions are known by the unlovely name of the Lower Rhyolitic Tuffs (LRT) and are the most important in our area, responsible for many of the scenic highlights.

The LRT rocks are a varied bunch. The simple description 'ash-flow tuffs' and 'air-fall tuffs' used by geologists, hides a vast variety of possible types of rock. This is evident when you walk out on these hills as the variety of rock types to be seen is almost overwhelming. The air-fall tuffs (where ash is thrown high into the atmosphere to fall around the area, falling thickly enough close to the vent(s) to form solid rock) are not very noticeable, with few distinguishing features, but these rocks form large parts of the area and can be seen at the top of the Llanberis Pass (between Pen y Pass and Pont y Gromlech) and on the Miners' Track (see Walk 1). They are 'massive' (i.e. not showing signs of bedding), with irregular cooling joints and some signs of slate-like layering known as 'cleavage' (see chapter 6), but otherwise unremarkable. However, it is possible to get a grip on some of the major types and/or features of volcanic rock of the LRT phase, in particular a type of rock known as 'breccia'.

When the magma and gases erupt to the surface, breaking through a fissure-vent, the explosive force often rips apart the rocks surrounding the vent and includes the lumps with the erupted material, thus leading to the formation of rocks called 'breccia' and the eruption may also include lumps of molten magma that solidify. A volcanic breccia is usually easy to spot because the lumps of rock within it are fairly angular. Where you come across a rock which contains lumps of other rocks, but the lumps are smooth and rounded, it is likely to be sedimentary in origin, not volcanic – for example the beds of small, rounded quartz pebbles found in the Cambrian Carnedd y Filiast Grits (chapter 2).

The volcanic breccias of the LRT in central Snowdonia are often very easy to see – especially around the southern margins such as near Craflwyn (Walk 9) and around Moel y Diniewyd, as well as on Snowdon (Walk 1), Carnedd y Cribau (Walk 7) and the Glyderau

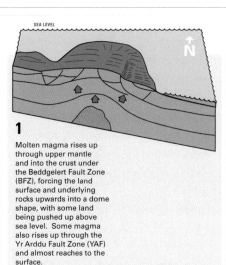

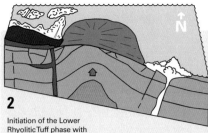

1

Molten magma rises up through upper mantle and into the crust under the Beddgelert Fault Zone (BFZ), forcing the land surface and underlying rocks upwards into a dome shape, with some land being pushed up above sea level. Some magma also rises up through the Yr Arddu Fault Zone (YAF) and almost reaches to the surface.

2

Initiation of the Lower Rhyolitic Tuff phase with eruption of basaltic lava to north and north-west of Bed-dgelert Fault Zone; eruptions took place both under sea (producing 'pillow' lavas and 'hyaloclastites') and above sea level, followed by later emplacement of dolerite (basaltic intrusive rock). The magma in the Yr Arddu Fault Zone then forced its way to the surface, erupting under sea level in a small caldera as 'ash-flow' eruption and forming 'welded tuffs'; more magma then makes its way up the fault, intruding between the still soft layers of welded tuff, but fails to reach the surface, becoming 'intrusive rhyolite' (near present day Yr Arddu and further north).

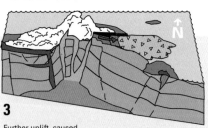

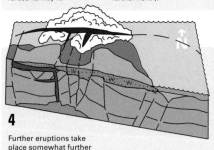

3

Further uplift, caused by production of more underground magma, and consequent movement along the Beddgelert Fault Zone leads to a collapse of the eastern flank of the dome and extensive flows of mud and 'megabreccia'.

This is followed by an eruption and subsequent pyroclastic flow on and around the same Fault Zone, depositing welded tuffs (present day Moel y Diniewyd and the south-eastern side of Snowdon).

4

Further eruptions take place somewhat further north and the caldera margin begins to take shape.

 Basalt* hyaloclastite, basaltic sandstone (BPF basa type)

 Sub LRTF sediments

 Magma

 Denote relative uplift and subsistence, respectively.

Reworked tuffs

Non-welded ash-flow tuff pyroclastic beccia

Welded ash-flow tuff

Yr Arddu Tuff (welded ash-flow tuff)

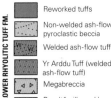 Megabreccia

Basalt* pillowed basalt hyaloclastite (Sub-LRTF basalt type)

Positions of block diagrams Relative to LRTF caldera and direction of view

Diagram 4.2 | The Snowdon Eruptive Cycle.

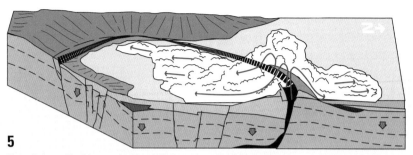

5

The main Lower Rhyolitic Tuff eruption occurs around present day Snowdon, Crib Goch, the Llanberis Pass and Carnedd y Cribau. A vast volume of material (60 million cubic metres) is emitted in ash-flow eruptions (including breccias). The voiding of the underground magma leads to a collapse of the ground around the caldera margin with the biggest drop around the northern area where the eruptions had occurred. Most of the material erupted is held within the caldera, but a further eruption of ash and other material pours out material to the east (towards present-day Dolwyddelan) and the north (towards present-day Conwy).

6

The top layers of the Lower Rhyolitic Tuffs are subject to erosion where they are above sea level and the eroded grains of rock are then laid down close on top of other LRT tuffs as sedimentary rock. Upward movement occurs underground, leading to emplacement within the LRT rocks of more intrusive rhyolite (though some of it reaches the surface as rhyolite lava).

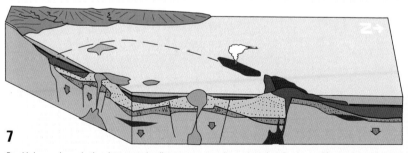

7

Basaltic lava and pyroclastic eruptions from vents around the caldera margin place the Bedded Pyroclastic Formation rocks with interspersed sedimentary rocks. More dolerite and rhyolite intruded into the LRT and BPF rocks. Not shown – further set of comparatively small pyroclastic (ash-flow) eruptions lay down the Upper Rhyolitic Tuffs and intrusion of quartz and minerals into cooling and fracture joints along boundaries between LRT and BPF, and between intrusive rhyolite and BPF (forming copper and lead mines).

(Walks 3, 4 and 5). The main LRT rocks in the northern areas of the caldera (around Crib Goch, the Llanberis Pass and Cwm Idwal) have clearly visible lumps of all sizes and shapes (see photos 4.2, 4.3, 4.4, w3.1, w7.3, w7.4 and w7.5). Breccias tend to be close to the fissure-vent where they were erupted as they don't travel far before falling to earth, while smaller particles ('ash') can be erupted high into the air or propelled for miles as 'flows' and 'surges'. The various types of breccia, although looking very different, are key ways of spotting the LRT rocks – however, to complicate matters, it is necessary to point out that lavas and 'intrusive' rocks (see paragraph after next) can also be 'brecciated', with lumps forming due to different rates of cooling, usually at the margins.

Another feature common to several types of volcanic rock is 'columnar-jointing' (where regular column-like patterns develop during cooling). This occurs in the LRT tuffs, intrusive rhyolites and other volcanic rocks (see photos 4.5 and w1.1).

Despite the incredible volume of expelled material, there was still a lot of magma which didn't manage to rise all the way to the surface. Instead it was intruded between the newly laid (and thus still soft) tuffs within and around the fissure-vents. These intrusions were extremely thick in some places (especially around the northern margins of the caldera) and were later exposed as overlying rocks were eroded and they add considerably to the overall significance of the LRT to the scenery of present day central Snowdonia (see diagram 4.3).

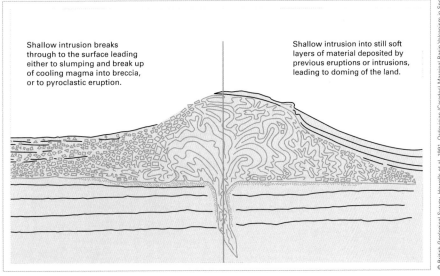

Shallow intrusion breaks through to the surface leading either to slumping and break up of cooling magma into breccia, or to pyroclastic eruption.

Shallow intrusion into still soft layers of material deposited by previous eruptions or intrusions, leading to doming of the land.

© British Geological Survey, Howells et al, 1991, Ordovician (Caradoc) Marginal Basin Volcanism in Snowdonia.

Diagram 4.3 | Intrusive and extrusive rhyolite.

Photo 4.2 | Lower Rhyolitic Tuffs, breccia, Cromlech Boulders, Llanberis Pass. This is a breccia from the LRT, with some pretty large lumps. The photo covers an area about 1.5m wide.

Photo 4.3 | Lower Rhyolitic Tuffs, breccia, near Bwlch y Moch – the large lump is about 13cm long and shows flow-banding indicating that it is probably originally intrusive rhyolite, later blasted away in an eruption.

Photo 4.4 | Lower Rhyolitic Tuffs, breccia, Mynydd Sygun – the large lump is about 40cm long.

Photo 4.5 | Lower Rhyolitic Tuffs columnar jointing, Cwm du'r Arddu – this is at the base of the LRT. Columnar jointing can also be seen in other types of volcanic rock (see photo w1.1).

The most noticeable of these scenic features is the knife-edge summit ridge of Crib Goch in the Snowdon horseshoe. Although the narrow nature of the ridge is a product of glaciation, the rocks which make up Crib Goch are formed from an intrusive rhyolite. Its reddish hue gives it its Welsh name, red ridge (Coch/Goch = red, Crib = ridge).

A useful feature to look for in rocks and which occurs commonly in the intrusive rhyolites is 'flow-banding'. These are lines left as the magma is intruded into other rock (see photos 4.6, 4.7, w4.4, w7.3). You can see many varieties of flow-banding on intrusive rhyolites in our area (see Walks 4, 7, 9 and 11). However, a word of warning is necessary as flow-banding can

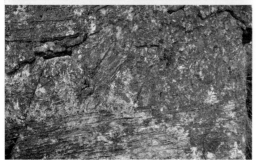

Photo 4.6 (top) | Flow-banding in intrusive rhyolite, Llanberis Pass (field of view about 1.25m across).

Photo 4.7 (middle) | Flow-banding in intrusive rhyolite, Llanberis Pass (field of view 0.75m across).

Photo 4.8 (bottom) | Disturbed flow-banding in rhyolite, Carnedd y Cribau. The lower bands have remained undisturbed, but the upper bands have been 'brecciated' (field of view 75cm across).

also appear in lavas (especially in the Lake District, but less commonly in Snowdonia), and it can sometimes look like bedding in sedimentary rocks or even the foliation of weathered welded tuffs. Sometimes you can see flow-banding in lumps within breccias (see photo 4.3) or, in other cases, the flowing rhyolite has been broken up by gravitational pull when it began to cool and settle, resulting in 'brecciated rhyolite' (see photo 4.8 and w7.4).

Photo 4.9 | Rhyolite, Craflwyn (field of view 75cm across).

As well as Crib Goch, the south-western flanks of Glyder Fawr and Glyder Fach also feature intrusive rhyolite, as does the low summit of Carnedd y Cribau and the hills (such as Moel Sygun) on the southern flank of Snowdon near Llyn Dinas (see photo 4.9). These hills, along with Crib Goch and the Llanberis Pass, represent the main fissure-vents and the boundaries of the collapsed caldera. Indeed, intrusive rhyolite is one of the most common types of rock you will come across in central Snowdonia. Its presence is also an indicator that you are very close to a fissure-vent.

Carnedd y Cribau shows these features very well indeed, but is less than 2,000 feet high, so it is one of those minor peaks that get overlooked by guidebooks and by walkers. But, like many slightly lower hills surrounded by bigger ones, it gives fantastic views of the surrounding heights, especially Snowdon, and displays many of the features of the Snowdonia eruptive cycle such as the northern and eastern edges of the Snowdon caldera (see Walk 7).

Traditionally geologists have left intrusive rocks out of the 'time column' of how the various rocks are assigned to different ages, but these intrusions were part and parcel of the LRT eruptive cycle. The tuffs and intrusive rocks have become incredibly hard rocks, resisting millions of years of erosion, and give us the key to understanding the raw material from which the landscape of Snowdon itself has been carved.

The LRT phase was followed by a period of erosion and sedimentation (as can be seen from diagram 4.2). Some of the volcanic material was erupted and laid down above sea level and was easily eroded in its early unconsolidated state, resulting in beds of 're-worked' 'tuffaceous' sandstones being deposited on the top of the LRT in some places (such as Carnedd y Cribau and Cwm Glas). The LRT phase was the climax and the subsequent phases represent the maturation and decline of the volcanic furnace beneath the crust of North Wales some 430 million years ago, but there were still some minor episodes of eruption to come.

The rocks produced in the eruptive phase after the LRT are traditionally known as the 'Bedded Pyroclastic Formations' (BPF). This is another unfortunate and misleading name as the eruptions that laid down these rocks were largely not pyroclastic but were mainly, although not exclusively, basaltic lava eruptions. The BPF eruptions took place at a few centres along the Beddgelert Fault Zone and the Hebog/Idwal Fault Zone.

The main BPF outcrops are found on the south-west flank of Glyder Fawr, around the summit and the eastern and southern flanks of Snowdon, Cwm Glas Mawr and Carnedd y Cribau. The individual rocks of the BPF are hard to distinguish. However the beds of the formation themselves are fairly easy to recognise from a medium distance, being distinctively darker than the underlying LRT and with conspicuous layers of bedding (see photos 4.10 and w7.6).

Photo 4.10 | Outcrop of the Bedded Pyroclastic Formation (BPF) near the junction of the Miners' Track and the Pig Track on Snowdon. The BPF consists of basaltic lava, tuffs and sedimentary rocks; the bedding is easy to spot (see also photo w1.2). The outcrop is about 2m high.

The transition to BPF is particularly clear on a number of the popular tracks heading up Snowdon – for example at the narrow point of Bwlch Main on the south ridge, on the Miners' Track shortly before it joins the Pig Track (see photo w1.2). Off the main tracks it can also be seen as you ascend from Cwm Glas Mawr into Cwm Glas (see photo 4.11) or Cwm Uchaf. The final ascent to the summit of Yr Wyddfa from Bwlch Glas, as well as the final section of the south ridge from Bwlch Main (all walking the routes up Snowdon converge on these two ridges), all bring you close up to the BPF.

Photo 4.12, taken in Cwm Glas, shows a 'dewatering' structure in rocks, formed from eroded volcanic sediments, laid down on wet sands following disturbance caused by earthquakes or eruptions. The weight of the newly laid, overlying sediments has caused them to drop down into the water-saturated sediments below, expelling the water and leaving these strange shapes in the modern day outcrops.

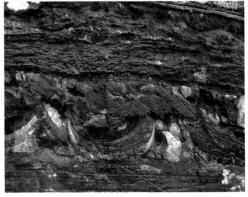

Photo 4.11 (top) | The boundary between the Lower Rhyolitic Tuffs and the Bedded Pyroclastic Formation is visible in this outcrop in Cwm Glas. The top of the LRT (here in the form of 'reworked' tuffs laid down as sediments) is capped by a layer of brecciated basalt.

Photo 4.12 (bottom) | 'De-watering' structure in sedimentary rock from 're-worked' (i.e. eroded and laid as sediments) material of the Lower Rhyolitic Tuffs, Cwm Glas. The later, upper beds have compressed water-saturated lower sedimentary beds until the water escapes by upwards movement at the upper edges of the curved, slumped sediments in the centre (field of view, 1m across).

The BPF phase also saw episodes of intrusion as a result of magma that didn't make it all the way to the surface. The basaltic equivalent of intrusive rhyolite is known as 'dolerite'. This is a very common rock in the area and once you get to know what it looks like is fairly easy to spot; however it lacks clear structural features such as bedding or flow-banding, featuring only a few drying cracks ('joints'). Its surface is often pitted and very uneven – it looks rather like a very bad plastering job (see photo 4.13) and it is this which is fairly easy to spot once you've become accustomed to seeing it. The Daear Ddu Ridge on the eastern side of Moel Siabod (an excellent and relatively safe, ridge scramble) is made of dolerite, as is the rock bar that retains Moel Siabod's glacial lake Llyn y Foel (see photo 6.13). It can also be seen in the Llanberis Pass (south-west of Pont y Gromlech), forming the long knobbly ridge of Creigiau Gleision in the Carneddau and the crags between Llyn y Adar and Llyn Llagi on the Moelwyn ridge, as well as many other places.

The BPF was followed by another set of pyroclastic eruptions, producing the 'Upper Rhyolitic Tuffs' (URT). Its outcrops are confined to a few places in the northern area of the Snowdon caldera and further east in the Dolwyddelan 'syncline'. As well as the small outcrop on the summit of Snowdon, the URT also occurs on the summit of Carnedd Ugain and the ridge leading to it, Crib y Ddysgyl, and there are some small outcrops along the ridge north-east of Y Lliwedd. As the walk along Crib y Ddysgl is a 'hands-on' scramble, you are guaranteed a close look at the rocks of the URT if you walk along this section of the Snowdon horseshoe on your way to the summit of Snowdon.

Photo 4.13 | A typical weathered dolerite outcrop (field of view 1m across).

Here, on the roof of Wales, on the summit of Snowdon (Copa 'r Wyddfa) if you look hard enough and are lucky, you can find traces of fossils in the rocks. I found a loose fossil just above the old summit café a few years back. It was a cloudy day and there were no views to be enjoyed, so unconsciously my attention was fully focused on where my feet were going when my eyes caught the distinctive pattern of shell markings. Clearly the small rock had been on the track for some time as there were several scratch marks, created as walkers had stepped on it, rubbing it against underlying rock. And clearly the shell markings have been distorted from their original shape, as if elongated to one side, probably by later mountain-building forces (see photo 4.14).

Photo 4.14 | Fossil from just below the summit of Snowdon (field of view 5cm diagonally from lower left to upper right).

Photo 4.15 | Fossils from the eastern side of Tryfan, near Nant Bochlwyd (the fossils are about 3cm across).

As the summit of Yr Wyddfa is the highest point in England and Wales it seems certain that the fossil cannot have come from above. So unless some person carried up and dropped it there, the implication (supported of course by fossils that can be seen embedded in the summit rocks) is that the summit of Snowdon was clearly once below sea level. I've also found fossils on the lower slopes of Tryfan (see photo 4.15).

The URT is a sequence of acidic ash-flow tuffs, bedded tuffs and tuffites (pyroclastic material mixed with other sediments from erosion of surrounding land), a few 'tuffaceous' siltstones and some basaltic beds. The URT period also saw some intrusions – such as the 'andesitic' intrusion (andesitic means mid-way between rhyolitic and basaltic) around Llyn Teryn, with its distinctive columnar joints (see photo w1.1). The joints can be seen from the Miners' Track, forming a rib of hard rock from above Llyn Teryn and stretching across Cwm Dyli (see photo 5.5). This intrusion is unusual in Snowdonia in that nearly all the other intrusions tended to be either rhyolitic or basaltic and there is otherwise little or no andesitic material (andesitic rocks, as the name implies, are common in the volcanic Andes range of South America).

There were later eruptions outside our area which are still considered to be part of the 2nd Eruptive Cycle but, by and large, the violent era of volcanicity in North Wales is over, except for one more minor series of events.

Sometime late in the 2nd Eruptive Cycle hot liquids were intruded into gaps in the rocks, injecting what became quartz and other rocks, sometimes containing minerals, such as copper. The quartz veins are found in many places, some quite large (for example on the lower slopes of Crib Goch and Y Lliwedd as seen from Cwm Llydaw on Walk 1), but more generally they are quite small, though often with a minor effect on the landscape (see photo 10.12). There are also several copper veins, which have been extensively mined, mainly occurring on the boundary between the LRT and the BPF, such as the Britannia mine on Snowdon (above Glaslyn) and Sygun mine near Beddgelert (open as a museum with underground tours). We will look a bit more closely at these mines in chapter 10 when considering the human influence on the landscape.

Once the Iapetus Ocean plate had been fully subducted underneath the continental plates of Avalonia and Laurentia volcanic activity ceased. But then another phase opened, as the two continental plates continued to be impelled into each other by the earth's underlying convection currents. What happened then is the subject of the next chapter.

CHAPTER 5

Mountains of Ash and Slate

Convection currents within the earth's mantle combined to drive Avalonia (and another chunk of proto-Europe, Baltica) towards Laurentia. The first result of this was the squeezing closed of the Iapetus Ocean and the volcanic activity that was generated as a result.

Once the ocean plate had been entirely subducted, the continents continued to move towards each other until their plates began to collide. Unlike the situation where a dense ocean plate subducts when it meets a less dense continental plate, when two equally dense continental plates collide there is often no subduction. Instead, as the internal forces of convection continue to drive the plates into each other, they start to fold, buckle and build mountains as they are forced upwards (the plate thickens downwards too and by more than it thickens upwards) – see diagram 5.1.

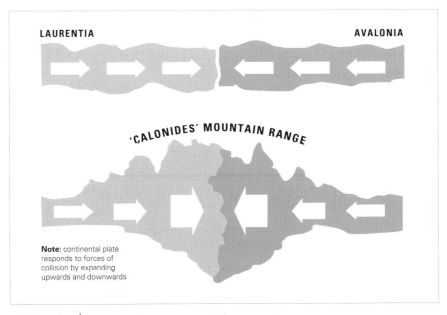

Diagram 5.1 | Continental plate collision and mountain-building.

The Alps are the product of the African continental plate colliding with the European plate, and the Himalayas the result of India's collision with Asia. The mountains built when Avalonia/Baltica and Laurentia collided some 400 million years ago were at least as high as the Alps and perhaps as high as the Himalayas. What we see today, impressive as they are, are just the last remaining vestiges, the stumps, of those massive mountains that were created during the geological eras that followed the Ordovician, known as the 'Silurian' and the 'Devonian'.

Anyone who has tripped and fallen against rock knows how hard and unforgiving it is contrasted with frail human flesh and bone. While it is tough, rock is also brittle. Smash it with a hammer and it will shatter into pieces. However, at depth, rock has another odd characteristic; subject to slowly accumulating pressure over very long periods of time, it becomes 'ductile' and can be folded. It behaves in a 'plastic' fashion.

The forceful collision of eastern Avalonia with Laurentia probably continued for some 20 to 30 million years after the Iapetus Ocean plate had fully disappeared through subduction. As marginally softer rocks were progressively pressed up against harder ones, the softer rocks started to fold, forming new shapes, with 'anticlines' and 'synclines'. Sometimes the pressures were so great that the folds buckled over and piled up on top of one another. This is what builds mountains.

Photo 5.1 | Anticline I: Marchlyn Bach.

Photo 5.2 | Anticline II: Llanberis Pass.

Sometimes the evidence is easy to see, but sometimes the results can be confusing to the present day viewer. Two anticlines are easily seen in our area in the sedimentary grits of the Cambrian era, one above Marchlyn Bach and another below the final peak on the Llanberis Ridge (halfway along Llyn Peris). These anticlines are easy to spot, but elsewhere the situation is more complex (see photos 5.1 and 5.2).

The succession of Cambrian sedimentary rocks is not straightforward on the south-western side of the Llanberis Pass, unlike on the other side, where the succession produced the regular pattern of grits, siltstones and more grits, resulting in high, low and more high relief (see chapter 2). The Llanberis Pass is the site of a fault, and pressure during the mountain-building period has affected the rocks unevenly on each side. On the western side the rocks have been pushed completely out of shape and even turned upside down.

The tougher volcanic rocks also folded in response to the collision of the continents but less sharply, forming shallower folds. The Snowdon volcanic area is marked by several great synclines, which often follow the old fault zones. The best known is the massive but gentle syncline that runs through Cwm Idwal, via Cwm Glas Bach and Cwm du'r Arddu, all the way to Moel Hebog, and which follows the western limit of the Snowdon caldera. The classic view of this syncline is from Cwm Idwal, with the visible succession of rocks from the Lower Rhyolitic Tuffs to the Bedded Pyroclastic Formation and some basalt lava above. Indeed, this

Diagram 5.2 + Photo 5.3 | Syncline I: Cwm Idwal.

is one of the great views in Snowdonia. The climb up or down from Cwm Idwal via Twll Du (the 'black chasm', known as the Devil's Kitchen), along one of the curves of the syncline, is one of the most exhilarating walks in Snowdonia (Walk 2) – see photo 5.3 and diagram 5.2.

A continuation of the same syncline can also be seen at the top of Cwm Glas Bach, just below 'Clogwyn Station' on the Snowdon Mountain Railway, and is best viewed from the Glyderau or the Llanberis Pass (see photo w11.5). Another superb view of the same syncline is

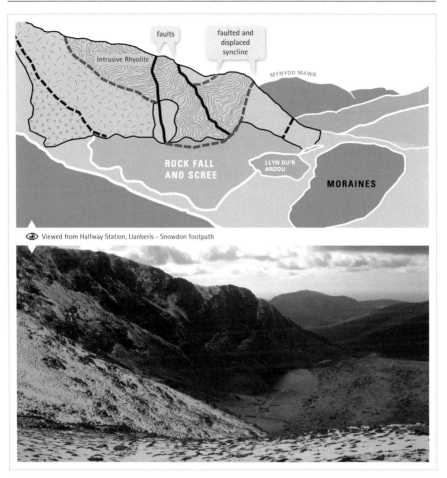

Diagram 5.3 + Photo 5.4 | Syncline II: Cwm Du'r Arddu.

found in Cwm du'r Arddu – one of the most magnificent cwms in Snowdonia. This view, however, is slightly confusing because a big fault and an intrusion have complicated the picture and Cwm du'r Arddu lacks the simple symmetry of Cwm Idwal. However the disrupted line of the syncline in section can still be traced (see photo 5.4 and diagram 5.3). A good overview of Cwm du'r Arddu can be had by leaving the Llanberis track where it turns to rise up to the Llanberis Ridge (6035 5627) and continuing straight on along a grassy, roughly level mining track to some ruins. A walk through the highly atmospheric cwm, among the fallen blocks of rock, is also highly recommended and allows for close study of many fascinating types of rock.

Photo 5.5 | Syncline III – see upper centre of photo, above Cwm Dyli. In the foreground, the rocks are outcrops of an andesitic intrusion which displays columnar jointing (see photo w1.1).

A syncline can also be seen on the Lliwedd Ridge on Snowdon – best seen from the Miners' Track (Walk 1) – see photo 5.5. These synclines and anticlines, along with clearly tilted beds of rocks, are some of the most obvious evidence for the immense forces that crumpled up the enormously tough volcanic rocks into massive mountains.

The power behind the mountain-building period was also responsible for another common phenomenon in the area – the creation of the slate beds of North Wales. We saw in Chapter 2 that the Llanberis slate beds were initially laid down as mudstones, and it was only much later that the mudstones were converted into slate. In fact this happened during the mountain-building episode at the end of the Silurian and beginning of the Devonian eras.

The original mudstones were formed from very fine particles or 'grains' laid down in mudflats in tidal conditions, with the eroded grains of rock settling in random patterns at all sorts of angles, eventually becoming cemented in place as solid rock.

However, when mountain-building pressures were applied to the rocks they were severely folded (see photo 5.6). In the same process the minerals making up the rock grains were transformed into a regular pattern, forming parallel planes (parallel to the main source of pressure). This is thought to have happened at a depth of about 6 to 7km below the earth's surface and at a temperature of around 250°C.

Photo 5.6 (top) | Convoluted bedding (and later dolerite intrusion) exposed in slate quarry, Llanberis.

Photo 5.7 (right) | Cleavage plane of slate exposed in a quarry face.

The new type of rock is liable to split along these planes, called the 'cleavage plane', between the now parallel minerals, thus splitting fairly cleanly to produce usable slate. Good quality slate cleaves very thinly making it ideal for roofing. One consequence of this is that fossils within the rocks are often destroyed, and another is that signs of the original bedding may also be lost (though this is not the case in the great quarry at Llanberis where bedding can still be distinguished).

The purple and blue-grey slates of the Llanberis slate formation are of particularly high quality (see photo 5.7), but only a few of the outcrops met the requirements for economic exploitation (thus the enormous waste tips associated with slate quarrying). Slate quarries of all different sizes exist in the greater Snowdonia area in every sedimentary formation. In our area the best slate is produced by the Llanberis slate formations, rocks dating from the Cambrian. But there are plenty of Ordovician slate quarries – such as those at Blaenau Ffestiniog.

Cleavage can also be identified in many other rocks in our area, including many of the volcanic tuffs, or at least those made up of fine fragments or 'ash'; large sections of the Lower Rhyolitic Tuffs are made up of air-fall ash tuffs with signs of cleavage (see photo w5.2). The nature of cleavage depends very much on the size of the mineral grains of the original sedimentary or volcanic rocks. Volcanic ashes are very small, so are susceptible to cleavage,

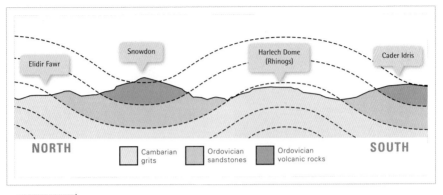

Diagram 5.4 | Simplified cross-section of geology, Snowdon-Rhinogs-Cader Idris.

as are mudstones. Sandstones and grits have big grains, thus they do not produce good cleavage – indeed it may well be entirely absent from many sandstones and grits, or it gives rough, uncontrollable breaks across thickly-spaced cleavage planes.

This turning of mudrock into slate is one form of the process known as 'metamorphosis'; the production of slates is known as 'low-grade' metamorphism. Another form is when rocks are 'cooked' by hot intruding rocks. This is responsible for two summits in our area, Moel Eilio and Foel Goch (the one in the Glyderau), where rhyolitic intrusions of 'microgranite' have hardened the surrounding and normally comparatively soft Ordovician siltstones (the Nant Ffrancon formation). This is why these summits are high points while the non-cooked sedimentary rocks around them are lower. The area of metamorphosed rock is known as a 'metamorphic aureole'.

The mountain-building episode we have been looking at is known to geologists as the 'Caledonian Orogeny'; Caledonian because it also created the mountains of the Scottish Highlands (and the Lake District, Ireland, Scandinavia and eastern North America). Orogeny because that is the word geologists have coined for mountain building.

The folds, with their anticlines and synclines, we see in central Snowdonia are only part of a much wider set of mountain-building features that link these areas. Snowdon's folds are also part of a wider regional pattern that stretches south to include the area known as the Rhinogs and, to its south, Cader Idris. The central Snowdonia area forms a 'synclinal' area with its corresponding 'anticlinal' area in the Rhinogs (also known as the 'Harlech Dome') and another great synclinal area embracing Cader Idris.

Having seen how Snowdon and its surrounding mountains were built up, it is now time to look at how it was carved into its present state, which means jumping from about 350 million years ago to just a few tens of thousands of years ago.

CHAPTER 6

Snowdon's Ice Age

The period between the end of the Caledonian mountain-building episode, about 400 million years ago, and the start of the Ice Ages, in much more recent times, has left little record in central Snowdonia of what happened during those intervening aeons.

For some of that time central Snowdonia was above sea level. During those periods a lot of material would have been eroded away, millimetre by millimetre, year by year, for millions of years, reducing the Alpine or Himalayan-sized mountains of the Caledonides range to a few hardened stumps, the mountains we see today. There were further tectonic events elsewhere on the earth which affected Snowdonia, such as the collision of Africa and Europe, but with much less far-reaching consequences.

We can assume that central Snowdonia was also almost certainly under sea level at other times. During these periods new sedimentary rocks would have been laid down.

However, if this did happen, there is no evidence to show it that it did and any rocks that were laid down have been entirely eroded away. For example, many geologists believe that the whole of Britain must have been below sea level during the era known as the 'Cretaceous' (from 145 million until 60 million years ago). This was the period during which the chalk formations were laid down and which today crop out in much of southern and eastern Britain. The present theory assumes that chalk was laid down over the whole of Britain and that it has been entirely eroded away from all those areas where older rocks are exposed, including central Snowdonia.

And so we will pass over 350 million years in fewer than 300 words, moving at breakneck speed to the near present and a timescale measured in thousands, rather than millions, of years.

There have been twenty different cold or 'ice' ages on the earth since 1,600,000 years ago, interspersed with temperate 'inter-glacial' phases. Plant remains from the temperate period between 100,000 years and 80,000 years ago have been uncovered in North Wales under the glacial deposits (known nowadays as 'till', though previously called 'boulder clay') of later ice ages. But, in general, each resurgent ice age wipes away the evidence of the effects of its predecessor on the landscape.

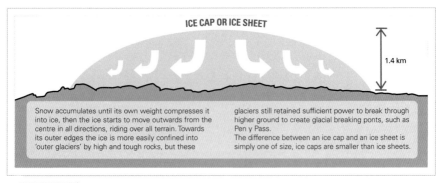

Diagram 6.1 | Ice cap/sheet

The last ice stage was at its most intense from 26,000 years to 11,500 years ago (though there was a short colder blip from 11,500 years to 10,000 years ago which led to a re-invigoration of glaciers in the highest cwms). During this period, first an ice 'cap' and then an ice 'sheet' developed a few miles to the south-east of Snowdon.

An ice cap is created as snow accumulates over several years. As the temperature falls and there is no summer melting, the snow gets deeper and deeper, building into a dome shape. The weight of the accumulated snow compresses the older layers of snow, eventually transforming the lowest layers into ice, which as even more weight is added, then starts to deform and to flow out in all directions (see diagram 6.1). At its centre an ice cap or sheet accumulates and spreads out over the land, regardless of the terrain. But as it flows further out, at its margins, it starts to become constrained by topography and develops major 'outflow glaciers', carving out deep troughs through any mountainous land it meets.

Some geologists argue that sufficient ice was created in central Snowdonia itself to account for the scenery, but it is generally believed that there was an ice sheet that covered North Wales, centred in the present-day Migneint area, an undulating region of moor and bog, with fairly low relief. About 18,000 years ago, at the height of the last ice age, the Migneint ice sheet was some 1,400 metres thick at the centre (this is higher than Snowdon is above present sea level at 1,085 metres).

The ice sheet overran the area around present day Snowdonia, subjecting the whole range of mountains to burial under ice, except for the very highest summits (such as Yr Wyddfa, Garnedd Ugain, Glyder Fawr, Glyder Fach and Elidir Fawr). These summit points ('nunataks' in the geologists' jargon) would have stuck up above the ice sheet rather like hill tops which protrude above a cloud inversion, but surrounded by the dirty white/grey colour of the ice sheet and its outlet glaciers (see photo 6.1).

The mass of ice thrust towards Snowdon by the power of the Migneint ice sheet found its path impeded by the lie of the high land, made up of tough volcanic rocks. But the accumulation of snow and ice in the Migneint was irresistible (see map 7.1). Its outlet glaciers cut major 'breaching' points, creating today's mountain passes.

Photo 6.1 | An outlet glacier of the Greenland ice sheet.
Photo John Simmons, © The Geological Society of London
www.geolsoc.org.uk

Map 6.1 | Ice flows in Snowdonia at the height of the last ice age.

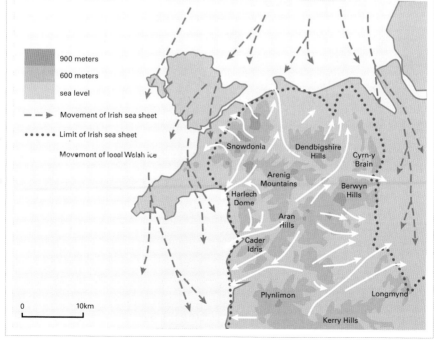

900 meters
600 meters
sea level
‑ ‑ ‑ ▶ Movement of Irish sea sheet
• • • • • Limit of Irish sea sheet
Movement of local Welsh ice

Snowdonia
Dendbigshire Hills
Cyrn-y Brain
Arenig Mountains
Berwyn Hills
Harlech Dome
Aran Hills
Cader Idris
Plynlimon
Longmynd
Kerry Hills

0   10km

The major breaching points were, from east to west: between the Glyderau and the Carneddau at present day Idwal Cottage (photo 6.2); at Pen y Pass (photo 6.3); at Bwlch Drws y Coed (leading into the Nantlle valley); and near Llyn Cwellyn. The first three of these points are all marked by some of Snowdonia's most overpowering scenery with narrow gorges cut straight through the mountains. This is most spectacularly seen in the steep mountain crags on either side of the Llanberis Pass below Glyder Fawr and Crib Goch, in the western face of Pen yr Ole Wen, opposite Cwm Idwal, and in the eastern face of Mynydd Mawr.

Photo 6.2 (top) |
Glacial breaching point at Ogwen Cottage.

Photo 6.3 (middle) |
Glacial breaching point at Pen y Pass.

Photo 6.4 (bottom) |
Secondary glacial breaching point, Llyn Cowlyd, Carneddau.

There were secondary breaching points too – on the Snowdon massif these were Bwlch y Saethau, Bwlch Cwm Llan, Bwlch Brwynog and Bwlch Maesgwm, and on the Glyderau at Twll Du (the Devil's Kitchen above Cwm Idwal), Cwm y Caseg Fraith and Bwlch Goleuni. Bwlch y Brecan, on the Glyderau Ridge below Foel Goch, was also a secondary breaching point, but here the ice flowed from the Nant Ffrancon side into Cwm Dudodyn and the lower Llanberis Pass. On the Carneddau there was a secondary breaching point between Pen Llithrig y Wrach and Creigiau Gleision (above Llyn Cowlyd Reservoir – photo 6.4), as is obvious today from the profile of the lower Carneddau as seen from Tryfan or the southern end of the Glyderau Ridge.

At these secondary breaching points, the ice found a way over the obstruction of the hard volcanic rock, but without cutting deep trench-like valleys. Instead it just left the cols that separate the present day summits of the Snowdon massif and the Glyderau. Each col or bwlch provides present day walkers, as they have to descend and re-ascend between summits, with excellent opportunities for pondering the fact that water, in the form of ice, is more powerful than rock (though the ice is dependent on cracks in the rocks and other weaknesses to start the process of breaking the rock up). These slopes also often provide an opportunity to study the changing beds of rocks – for example the climb from Bwlch y Brecan to the summit of Y Garn crosses a succession of rock types, several volcanic and some sedimentary, illustrating the way in which the area's unique geological history has ended up providing us with so many great walks, walks that cross over millions of years of rock of many different types and is now exposed by glaciation.

The landscape of Snowdonia is finally getting close to its present form. But the declining years of the last ice age were of vital importance in adding some key stages in the etching of the modern shape of central Snowdonia.

From about 18,000 years ago temperatures started to rise again and from then until about 12,000 years ago, 'cwm glaciers' poured out of hollows high in the mountains (see photos 6.5 and 6.6) The ice that flowed out of these glacial 'cwms' (or 'corries' or 'cirques') fed larger 'valley glaciers' in the trenches cut by the outlet glaciers (see photos 6.7, 6.8, 6.9 and 6.10). These cwm glaciers became the key agents of glacial sculpting of the present-day landscape, deepening the work of earlier glacial periods. This period of just 6,000 years was to see some of the most intense glaciation in the area and to leave many of the most magnificent aspects of today's scenery. The scenery at the time was no doubt reminiscent of the Alps and other ranges today (except in scale of mountains), with year round snow and steep glaciers, often marked by ice falls (the glacier's equivalent of a waterfall).

As with the ice cap, glaciers form when the accumulation of snow, in a hollow or gully on a mountain-side, exceeds the rate of snow loss (or 'ablation'), and it is turned first to a

Photo 6.5 | Cwm glacier, Tour du
Mont Blanc. Photo Reg Atherton

Photo 6.6 | Foel Goch and Cwm Coch,
northern Glyderau. A glacier would have
tumbled out of the cwm just as in photo 6.5.

form of ice known as 'firn' and then to ice proper. As it accumulates and gets heavier, the firn
starts to cut down into the underlying rock, forming features known as 'nivation cirques', the
immature form of glacial cwm. A flowing cwm glacier develops when firn becomes ice and,
under pressure of its own accumulating weight, begins to deform and to cut more deeply

Photo 6.7 | Valley glacier, Himalayas,
Pakistan, fed from the side by cwm
glaciers. Photo Ian Smith

Photo 6.8 | Nant Ffrancon and former glacial
cwms on the left which would have fed
extra ice into the valley glacier responsible
for the wide, flat floor of the valley.

Photo 6.9 | Valley glacier, Himalayas, Pakistan. Photo Ian Smith

Photo 6.10 | The Llanberis Pass.

into the underlying rock and then to move downhill. The glacier becomes a flowing river of ice. The speed of flow may be slow compared with an ordinary river, but is immensely more powerful (see diagram 6.2).

The processes involved cause the ice to abrade and destroy the surrounding land. The glacier 'quarries' rock from below (exploiting joints and other weaknesses), then carries the quarried blocks away embedded in the ice. These rocks act to pluck out more rocks as the glacier flows, deepening its channel. The process leads to unstable rock walls, which then experience 'over-steepening' as rocks high up are undermined and come crashing down; this

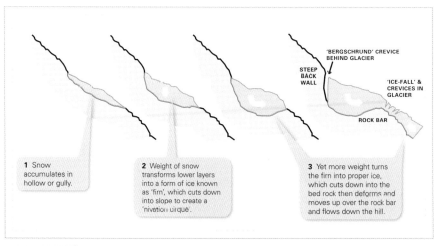

Diagram 6.2 | Development of cwm glaciers.

waste is carried away on the surface of the glacier. All the material carried away by the glacier is later dumped to become 'till' (previously known as 'boulder clay'), 'moraines' or 'erratics'.

The seat of the glacier digs into the mountain side, creating in tough rock the classic glacial landscapes of a glacial cwm with steep 'headwalls' and 'sidewalls', and often a 'rock bar' at the exit to the cwm. Glaslyn is a good example (see photos 6.11 and 6.12). The rock bar extends upwards into the ridge variously known as Y Gribau and Y Gribin, providing the walker with a fine, but steep, scramble. Such rock bars can be identified widely throughout wider Snowdonia, including Llyn y Foel (below Moel Siabod – see photo 6.13 and diagram 6.3) and Llyn Cau (on Cader Idris). However, it depends on the geology whether a rock bar develops or not, and under certain circumstances cwms develop without rock bars (see next chapter on cwms in the Glyderau).

Photo 6.11 (top) | The Snowdon staircase of glacial cwms: from bottom to top, Cwm Llydaw, Cwm Glaslyn and Upper Glaslyn.

Photo 6.12 (middle) | Glaslyn and its enclosing rockbar.

Photo 6.13 (bottom) | Llyn y Foel (below Moel Siabod). The rock bar, made of dolerite, can be seen crossing in front of the lake and running all the way up to where the photo was taken and beyond to the summit.

Map 6.2 |

Snowdon's glacial cwms.

Photo 6.14 | The Snowdon
Horseshoe from the start
of the Crib Goch Ridge; Crib
Goch and Crib y Ddysgyl
form an arête, with glacial
cwms carved into the rock
on either side, leaving the
classic knife-edge ridge.

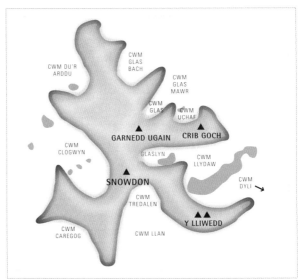

Snowdon's dramatic shape, with its many rewarding walks, is a product of ice carving out the glacial cwms and valleys in hard resistant rock that produces sharp edges and extremely steep slopes. Ridges radiate from Snowdon's common sloping summit plateau with Garnedd Ugain. Between the ridges, which are sometimes narrowed into knife-edge 'arêtes', sit the great cwms. It is this mixture of ridge and cwm that gives Snowdon its particular magnificence. Fittingly for the highest mountain in Wales it offers the walker the opportunity to delight in some of the best glacial scenery in the British Isles.

The Snowdon Horseshoe (encompassing a 'staircase' of four glacial cwms) is the centrepiece of Snowdonia's outstanding rock architecture. A walk around the Horseshoe – out on the Pig Track, Miner's Track or the knife-edge ridge of Crib Goch, and back over Y Lliwedd – is truly memorable (see photos 6.11 and 6.14) – see Walk 1.

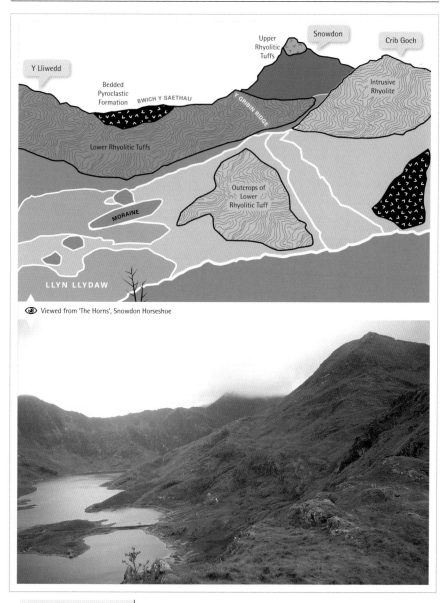

Viewed from 'The Horns', Snowdon Horseshoe

Diagram 6.4 & Photo 6.15 | Lower left, Llyn Lydaw. Left centre, Y Lliwedd. Centre right (hidden in cloud), Snowdon. Top right, Crib Goch. The terrace halfway down the side of Crib Goch is carved into the Bedded Pyroclast Formation, with intrusive rhyolite above and Lower Rhyolitic Tuffs below; the terrace also marks the upper limit of the Llyn Llydaw glacier and today carries the Pig Track.

All the standard routes up Snowdon provide both a bird's eye overview, looking down into the glacial cwms from the higher reaches. The lower parts of the routes also bring the walker closer to the detail of glaciation – 'moraines' (mounds of rock, now usually covered with vegetation, left, for example, by 'retreating glaciers'), 'roches moutonées' (rock outcrops smooth on one side and craggy on the other) and 'rock steps' (differences in height in a valley where two glaciers joined and deepened the valley floor in a sharp step). A walk lower down also brings a different perspective on the rock formations. Both high and low parts of the walks provide a chance to assess the scale of work done by the cwm glaciers of the last few thousand years of the ice age. To gaze upwards is as important as casting an eye downwards in gaining a feel for the power of ice. The depth of the cwms is perhaps best appreciated from the Miners' Track between Llyn Llydaw and Glaslyn.

Lowest and widest of the staircase of cwms is Cwm Dyli, with Llyn Teryn cupped away in a corner (best seen from the Miners' Track), and unfortunately scarred by a modern intrusion – a highly conspicuous pipeline feeding a hydraulic power station in Nant Gwynant (see photo 10.13). Lines of moraines run east-west across the Cwm Dyli marking stages in the 'retreat' of the glacier as rising temperatures moved in phases regularly shifting the melting point closer back to the source. An andesitic intrusion forms the jagged rock step at the back of Cwm Dyli, from near Llyn Teryn (see photo 6.5). The ice has plucked the rock away from the front of the andesite leaving nearly vertical walls. These andesite crags are easily seen on the recommended walk on Snowdon on the Miners' Track (Walk 1) where they display some very clear 'columnar jointing' (see photo w1.1). The crags could be described as very large 'roche moutonées', that common feature of glacial areas, where a smooth rounded shape faces 'upstream' and a craggy, plucked one 'downstream'.

The broad base of Cwm Dyli was scooped out by the glaciers pouring out of Cwm Llydaw immediately above it and further up comes Cwm Glaslyn, both containing glacial lakes. Cwm lakes can be quite deep. Glaslyn is 40 metres deep and Llyn Llydaw, 57 metres at its deepest point. The Pig Track runs on a shelf high above Cwm Llydaw, where softer 'Bedded Pyroclastic Formation' rocks are sandwiched between the tougher Lower Rhyolitic Tuffs (below) and intrusive rhyolite (above). This shelf also marks the rough height of glacier in Cwm Llydaw, which not only poured out through Cwm Dyli, but also breached the ridge at Bwlch y Moch, below Crib Goch's eastern ridge, to pour down northwards into the Llanberis Pass (see photo 6.15 and diagram 6.4).

Eventually the temperature started to rise again, until only the highest points could sustain the cold conditions needed to support a glacier. It was in this late stage that Upper Glaslyn came into being (see photo 6.11). It is often missed by walkers hauling up the last

Photo 6.16
Y Lliwedd, a
glacial arête.

stages of the Pig Track, but is well worth a short detour to peer over a retaining wall (erected as part of the mining operations here, so very great care needs to be taken moving into and out of the area). From the threshold of the tiny cwm, peering down at Glaslyn below and Llyn Llydaw below that, it is easy to get a feel of the retreating staircase of glaciers of the recent past. Here was the seat of the last remnants of glaciation in the Snowdon Horseshoe.

Undoubtedly among of the scenic masterpieces of the Snowdon Horseshoe are the 'arêtes' of Crib Goch and Crib y Ddsgyl on the northern side. The somewhat less sharp-edged ridge of Y Lliwedd on the southern side is no less magnificent a viewpoint – and for the landscape gazer probably provides a less distracting point on which to sit and wonder at the mixture of rock and water laid out before you (see photo 6.16). Crib Goch and Crib y Ddsygl got their shape as glaciers, on one side in the Horseshoe and on the other side in Cwm Uchaf and Cwm Glas, all cut back into the head and side of their cwms, leaving the sharp ridge and its exhilarating walk (see photo 6.14).

Snowdon's other great cwms, Cwm Glas Mawr, Cwm Glas Bach, Cwm du'r Arddu, Cwm Clogwyn, Cwm Caregog, Cwm Llan and Cwm Merch should not be overlooked and all are worth exploring if you have the time and experience to veer off the tracks and navigate your own route (except Cwm Llan which is on Watkin Path), especially on days when the clouds cover the summits.

From the Llanberis Pass, or from above it on the flanks of Glyder Fawr, the route up through Cwm Glas Mawr to Cwm Uchaf ('upper cwm') and Cwm Glas looks impossible for anyone other than climbers (see photo 6.17). But despite appearances there are some routes for those prepared to scramble up steep slopes – though be warned that going into the higher

Photo 6.17

Cwm Glas Mawr, Cwm Glas and Cwm Uchaf – three glacial cwms cut into the sharp eastern face of Garnedd Ugain and Crib Goch. Centre left is Cwm Beudy Mawr, part of the Llanberis Pass breaching point rather than the seat of a glacier.

reaches is a serious undertaking and should be done only in clear weather. There are only a few safe routes out and these are hard to find, and as there are dangerously steep crags above and below on all sides a minor navigational error could be catastrophic.

Standing near the cliff edge of high up in Cwm Glas, looking down into Cwm Glas Mawr immediately below and to the Llanberis Pass beyond, you can imagine the ice tumbling out of the inner cwm, cracked open in a mass of crevices, just like an ice fall seen in the Alps. Just as Upper Glaslyn was the seat of the final glacier to develop on Snowdon, so the glaciers of Cwm Uchaf and Cwm Glas came into existence at a late stage, when conditions were no longer sufficiently cold to sustain the seat of a glacier lower down in Cwm Glas Mawr. Here, and in the Snowdon Horseshoe, and especially in winter, the ice age is almost palpable. It becomes easy to appreciate the concept that we may well be in a temporary warm period between spells of widespread ice.

Around Crib Goch and Cwm Glas Mawr we are walking above the fissure-vents where the biggest eruptive episode of the LRT took place, the eruptions that led to the collapse of the Snowdon caldera. Here too is the most dramatic evidence of glaciation. Other areas also underwent mountain building pressures and ice ages, but in other places softer rocks have produced softer landscapes. It is Snowdon's tough volcanic tuffs and intrusive rocks, and the resistance they put up to glacial carving, that makes its scenery so stark, so demanding of attention.

Cwm du'r Arddu is another of nature's quarry tips (see photos 5.4 and 6.18). The wind often rushes through in force, whipping the lake up into sizeable waves and even raising a shower of spray that moves across the lake and up the hillside at the far end. It is little over an hour's walk from Llanberis, but aeons away in atmospheric intensity.

Cwm Tregalan sits high up in a corner of Cwm Llan and is what geologists call a 'parasite' on it. The glacier in Cwm Tregalan was one of the very late, high glaciers on Snowdon, carving itself a nook and leaving a moraine, nearly 50 metres high and 700 metres long, with a steep drop down into Cwm Llan proper. Some geologists believed that this was a feature known as a 'protalus rampart', where blocks of rock fell off the crags and slid across ice at the bottom of the slope to form a mound. But this view is now discounted and Cwm Tregalan seems likely to have held its own glacier, though probably a quite small one (see photo 6.19).

Photo 6.18 (top) | Cwm du'r Arddu.

Photo 6.19 (bottom) | Cwm Llan and Cwm Tregalan from Snowdon's south ridge. The moraine created by a small glacier within Cwm Tregalan is clearly visible running from left to right across the centre of the lower part of the photo.

There are also four minor, immature, cwms in the hollow formed by Cwm Dwythwch at the northern end of the Snowdon massif (see photo w12.1). These are probably remnants of glaciers that started to form quite late in the ice age and none is really well developed. But they do give an idea of how cwm glaciers are created in weaknesses on a mountainside.

The walk into Cwm Dwythwch is highly atmospheric (Walk 12). Sitting below the moraine that dams the lake looking at the curving rockwall below the ridge, the feeling is one of great remoteness, despite being only a few hundred metres from a farm track. A walk around the immature cwms below the ridge is detailed in the recommended walks section. The walk along the ridge is also excellent (especially in an anti-clockwise direction for views to Snowdon), but the views down into the cwms from the ridge fail to convey any real idea of the scale of the hollows carved out by these immature glaciers.

Cwm Clogwyn, on Snowdon's western flank, is unusual in that most cwms in central Snowdon are north-east facing (see photos 0.2 and 6.20). But Snowdon's extra height meant that snow and ice could accumulate, in quantities necessary to produce glaciers, even on the western face. The upper cwm is remote and wild, especially from within its enclosing arms. Three small lakes are held within the inner cwm (see photo 6.20 which shows two of them).

Photo 6.20 (right) | Cwm Clogwyn, from Rhyd Ddu track.

Photo 6.21 (bottom) | Snowdon summit (centre); Cwm Clogwyn (centre right), from the Snowdon Ranger track.

There are several moraines too, one of which is exposed on one side, showing what a moraine looks like under the post-glacial covering of soil and vegetation sported by most moraines in our area. The inner cwm has a 'threshold', the product of a tough dolerite intrusion, which holds it 100 metres above the outer cwm where two more lakes remain in existence.

A few years ago, I camped one night in Cwm Clogwyn at about 500 metres above sea level. We pitched our tents on the edge of the threshold of the cwm, just in front of Llyn Nadroedd, the most westerly and by far the prettiest of the three lakes nestling in the upper cwm. It was towards the end of one of those extremely hot summers. Moel Eilio and Moel Cynghorion were swathed in a cotton wool-like cloud that clung close to the surface, echoing the shape of the underlying hills (see photo 6.22). Then, as the sun began to set and the night drew in, waves of humid mist rolled in from the west. Wave after wave moved slowly forward, first engulfing the land below the cwm, removing from view two further glacial lakes lower down. Then the wave slowly crept up the lower slopes towards our wild campsite, finally reaching and encompassing us. Then a few minutes later the wave would pass and everything would be clear again, until the next wave approached, so it went on until dark. The next morning it was cloudy in the cwm, but as we climbed out onto the Llechog Ridge to go up to the summit of Yr Wyddfa, we pierced the cloud top and came out above an inversion, with dense white cloud below and blue sky above.

Photo 6.22

Cloud drapes Moel Eilio, late evening (view from Cwm Clogwyn).

The evening before, as I watched the clouds of mist rolling in, I had noticed a row of stone piles. They were clearly the remains of supports for a leat that channelled water from the lake for use in powering machinery in the slate quarry much further down the mountainside. Even in this distant and seldom visited spot, all the essentials of the landscapes of Snowdonia were

Photo 6.23

Ceunant Mawr
waterfall, Llanberis.
Photo Reg Atherton

visible – from evidence of volcanoes to the effects of glaciation, from weathering and erosion caused by the atmosphere, to the influence of human beings.

Snowdon's glacial cwms and the glacial trenches, such as the Llanberis Pass, are evidence that short term fluctuations of climate can affect the landscape as much as the great tectonic events. Vast volumes of rock were carried away by the glaciers, with 'erratics' from central Snowdonia carried as far as Anglesey.

The melting of the great valley glaciers has left the sides of the unveiled gorges pockmarked with 'hanging valleys' (at the height where their smaller glaciers flowed into the main ice) and subsequent waterfalls. There are many fantastic waterfalls evident along the Llanberis Pass after heavy rain (see photo 6.23). Slim torrents pour down the sheer rock faces that line Cwm Glas Bach and Cwm Glas Mawr, as well as the Glyderau side of the ridge. On that side of the valley, there are fine waterfalls on either side of Esgair y Ceunant as well as alongside the track between Llyn y Cwn (between Glyder Fawr and Y Garn) and Nant Peris. The waterfalls may be almost inconspicuous in dry weather, but after a spell of rain they command the attention of the walker as they pour out of their hanging valleys and down the hillsides in white torrents.

The descent of the Llanberis Pass – best of all on foot – ranks with a journey down through Scotland's Glencoe in drama and portent. The mass of rubble and scree that litters the slopes of the gorges, most conspicuously near Pen y Pass on the north-eastern side of the Pass, has all fallen since the glaciers melted (see photos w11.2 and w11.3). These scree slopes of the upper reaches of the Llanberis Pass almost seem like an echo of the quarry waste at the lower end of the Pass – nature's own quarry waste tips (Walk 11).

The cliffs here are today popular with climbers, presenting them with airy, exhilarating climbs. Some of the fallen blocks have also become popular with exponents of a variant of the climber's art, 'bouldering'. Boulderers can frequently be seen clinging to the massive blocks of rock, and which edge out onto the road, just south of the road bridge, Pont y Gromlech. These massive blocks are examples of one of the characteristic 'Lower Rhyolitic Tuff' rocks (breccia) and are well worth close examination – which can of course be carried out from a safe position standing on the ground and without the need to involve the spider-imitating, gravity-defying postures of boulderers (see photo 4.2).

Climbing has its fashions. A few years back it was other cliffs that were popular – the Idwal Slabs or Cwm du'r Arddu, for example. Perhaps even within the lifetime of this book the climbers will seek out newer challenges elsewhere. Whatever the developments of climbing fashion, on a longer time scale, the fallen rocks of the Llanberis Pass will be available for inspection for a long time to come. However, even that time period will come to an end if another ice age does come and glaciers return to this area. Then all those massive blocks of rock littering the slopes of the Llanberis Pass and other major troughs will be swept away like crumbs from the table and the shape of the landscape will be wrought anew.

CHAPTER 7

The Glyderau and Glaciation

The summit of Yr Wyddfa – Snowdon – is surrounded by glacial cwms. The glaciers have cut back into the mountain and eroded it into a star shape with narrow ridges emanating from the twin summits (see map 6.2). The Glyderau ridge is also heavily scarred by glacial cwms, but all of these cwms cluster on the same side of the ridge. Certainly the ridge holds a lot of glacial cwms – fifteen in all, and each of them situated on the north-eastern facing side (apart from Marchlyn Mawr and Marchlyn Bach which are off the main ridge, but still manage to face north-east).

The line of thirteen cwms on the main ridge, running from just north of Capel Curig to the slate tips of Bethesda quarry, is one of the most impressive sights in Snowdonia, with the complex of glacial cwms (Idwal, Cneifion, Bochlwyd and Clyd) at the central hinge point (see photo 7.1).

Cwm Idwal is the main glacial cwm of the complex of cwms at the centre of the Glyderau Ridge, centred on a great syncline (see photo 7.2). The upper cwms that surround it, Bochlwyd, Cneifion and Clyd, all fed ice into Cwm Idwal. Within Cwm Idwal itself there is a complex set of moraines, some up to 30 metres high. One set almost crosses the lake dividing the cwm into two (see photo w2.5).

Photo 7.1
Cwm Bochlwyd
(centre left); Cwm
Idwal (centre
right), Y Garn and
Cwm Clyd (upper
centre-right);
Cwm Cywion
(upper right). See
also diagram 7.1.

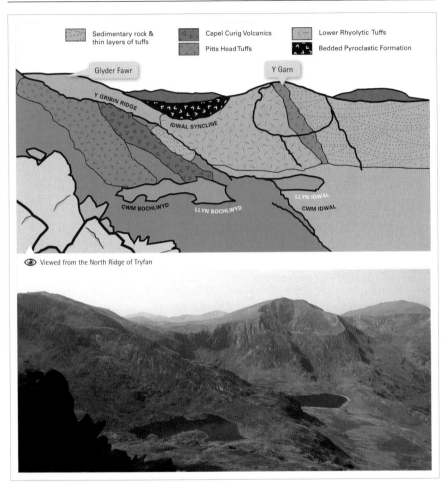

Diagram 7.1 + Photo 7.2 | Cwm Bochlwyd (centre left); Cwm Idwal (centre right).

The main Cwm Idwal glacier cut back into the mountain, leaving behind a rock headwall which is one of the scenic highlights of Snowdonia – Twll Du (the Black Chasm) or the Devil's Kitchen. Strictly speaking, Twll Du is the dark, dank gash in the centre of the headwall, but it is often used as a name for the whole rockwall and the spectacularly clear syncline or fold in the rocks that is made evident for all to see (see photo 5.3).

The row of cwms along the north-east facing arm of the Glyderau Ridge (from the north to south: Ceunant, Graianog, Perfedd, Bual, Coch, Cwyion and Clyd) is another scenic masterpiece, and also illustrates some interesting geological features (see photo 7.3 and diagram 7.2).

Map 7.1

Northern Glyderau cwms and geology map.

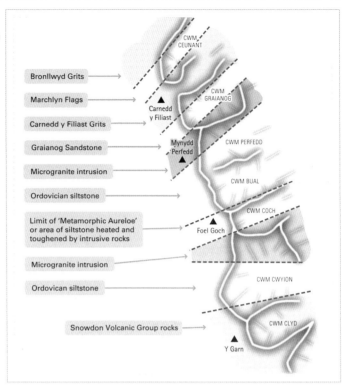

We saw, aeons ago in chapter 2, while looking at the Cambrian and Ordovician sedimentary rocks, that these rocks were fairly easy to identify on the northern end of the Glyderau Ridge as there was an orderly succession with, for example, the somewhat softer Marchlyn Flags forming a low point between the much tougher bands of (older) Bronllwyd Grits and (younger) Carnedd y Filiast Grits. These rocks and other younger volcanic rocks – all tilted so as to be next to one another rather than on top of another – lie in a row from north to south, with the northern cwms cutting across their boundaries (see map 7.1). The various rock types account for the variety of shapes seen in these cwms.

All the cwms form 'hanging valleys', entering the main valley some way up its side (see photos 6.7 and 6.8). Each cwm glacier was pretty short, rapidly seeing its ice tumble over the threshold of the steep lower slope into the valley glacier, and each cwm is sited where it is because of aspects of the succession of rocks.

The row of cwms can be seen from below on the minor road that runs along the bottom of the ridge or from the top of the ridge. But best of all is to combine a walk along the top

of the ridge with a rough, tough traverse along the 'thresholds' of the cwms, the line where the cwms open onto a steep slope to the valley floor. This is a long, hard and partly trackless walk, with some steep slopes to be traversed, but it gives an intimate view of the cwms from the inside and offers the best way of seeing and appreciating the detail of why each cwm is sited where it is and why it is shaped as it is (Walk 8).

It is unusual for cwms to occur in this sort of formation, running along a section through a succession of rocks (the 'strike' in geologists' jargon). Cwms often develop 'rock bars' at their threshold as the seat of the glacier digs downwards (Glaslyn is the classic example), but this feature is absent from the northern Glyderau cwms as the glaciers have sliced through areas of weaker rock in line with the rock boundaries (see map 7.1).

Starting in the north, with the oldest Cambrian rocks, Cwm Ceunant is centred on the softer Marchlyn Flags, with the tougher Bronllwyd Grits and Carnedd y Filiast Grits on either side. Clearly the glacier found the softer flags provided a weakness that could easily be enlarged into a cwm (see photo 7.4).

Next along, Cwm Graianog has the tough Carnedd y Filiast Grits on one side, forming the highest rock walls of all the northern cwms, stretching some 200 metres from cwm floor to the top of the rock wall (see Photos 1.10 and w8.2). This great rock wall is formed of the slabs of bedding in the Carnedd y Filiast Grits. Next comes an Ordovician sedimentary rock, the Graianog sandstone, and it is followed by an intrusion of rhyolitic igneous rock (a 'microgranite'). This is tougher than the sandstones, as are the grits on the other side. So, the cwm was first established on a thin seam of the weaker sandstones in the middle and on its junctions with tougher rocks. The outcrop of Graianog sandstones is narrow, thus Cwm Graianog is deep and narrow, rather than a classic roundish shape.

Photo 7.4 (opposite)
Glacial cwms on
the northern stretch
of Y Glyderau.

Photo 7.5 (right)
Cwm Graianog
moraines, seen
from above.

Photo 7.6 (bottom)
Cwm Perfedd
moraines, seen
from above.

From the inside, the cwm is highly atmospheric, with great tumbles of rocks, apparently jumbled all over the place. But in fact these great piles of rocks have been manoeuvred by the retreating glacier into a complex set of moraines (best seen from above). The moraine which runs along the cwm threshold, leaving a narrow gorge-like exit for the stream, has its own name, the Maiden's Arm, so impressive is it (see photos 7.5 and w8.2).

The intrusive microgranite is succeeded by the comparatively soft Nant Ffrancon silt-stones and mudstones. The result is that the next two cwms, Cwm Perfedd and Cwm Bual have soft, eroded headwalls, rounded shallow cwm floors and a similarly eroded common side wall separating them, a blunt, whale-back hump rather than a narrow arête. The granodiorite provides a steep northern sidewall to Cwm Perfedd, but the siltstones form the low headwalls of the long col between Mynydd Perfedd and Foel Goch, called Bwlch y Brecan, a distinctly low point along this section of the Glyderau Ridge, 100 metres lower than the summits on either side. Several moraines are easily seen in both cwms from higher viewpoints (see photos 7.6 and w8.3).

The southern side of Cwm Bual has an extremely steep sidewall, peaking in the summit of Foel Goch (see Photo 1.17). However, Foel Goch is made of the same Nant Ffrancon Formation mudstones and siltstones, but it is decidedly in great contrast to softer landscape. What has happened is that next in line, going further south, is another intrusion (intrusive rhyolite and microgranite). In chapter 6 we looked at the process of metamorphosis, where heat and/or pressure can cause changes to the mineral structure of rocks. Intrusions, which are molten when they are intruded, can have this effect.

The area of affected rocks around an intrusion is known as a 'metamorphic aureole'. That is what has happened here (and a similar process also affected the summit area of Moel Eilio the other side of the Llanberis valley). The rhyolite/microgranite intrusion has heated up the surrounding rocks into which it was intruded. The heating has altered their structure and toughened them up considerably. The result is the complete contrast in steepness and height between two parts of the same original rocks, with the normally soft Nant Ffrancon rocks, here toughened to form a steep, high sidewall to the southern side of Cwm Bual.

The next cwm, Cwm Coch, is another narrow, rock-filled cwm which has incised its narrow shape along the weakness created by the boundary between the two sets of tough rock, the microgranite intrusion and the beds of the metamorphosed Nant Ffrancon Formation. The absence of weak rocks accounts for its narrow profile, the cwm having been constrained to the area around the rock boundary. This is another highly atmospheric cwm with great tumbles of fallen rocks and steep, high sidewalls and headwall.

The intrusive rocks form a long arm which helps to enclose the next cwm in the row, Cwm Cwyion (the track continues along this arm suspended halfway up, with scree below and rocks above, leading eventually into the cwm; a superb, but slightly vertiginous path). The microgranite intrusion, Y Llymllwyd, forms the northern sidewall of the Cwm Cwyion, a narrow ridge with spectacular views towards Cwm Idwal, Tryfan and the Carneddau (see photo 7.7).

The cwm itself is centred on weaker beds of sedimentary rocks, thus creating another cwm with a lower headwall than sidewalls. The southern sidewall is formed by the successive layers of both the Llewelyn and Snowdon Volcanic Groups (see photo w8.4). Cwm Cwyion is the only cwm with an inner bowl enclosed by arms of tougher rock stretching out from the sides of the cwm. This gorge is just above the threshold of the cwm, and also the slope beneath the threshold becomes noticeably less steep around here.

I spent six or seven hours on a navigation exercise in this cwm a while back on a day of pouring rain and gale force winds, pacing from one contour blip to another, so I have a rather more intimate knowledge of this inner cwm than is needed to appreciate its general glacial

Photo 7.7

Y Llymllwyd – a glacial arête between Cwm Coch (lower left) and Cwm Cwyion (centre right), made of tough intrusive microgranite.

features and I will always remember the relief that came when a tiny lake appeared out of the mist, confirming that we were on route.

None of the other northern cwms we have looked at so far has a lake, as occurs in most of the Snowdon cwms and as well as Cwm Idwal, Cwm Clyd and Cwm Bochlwyd. Cwm Cwyion can claim a lake, but it is a pretty modest affair, accompanied by one or two large puddles nestling beside a fallen rock (see photo w8.4). But the bowl of low ground between these patches of water is soggy and boggy. A moraine stands proud of the bog level, almost certainly left by the final stage of the cwm glacier before it melted away at the end of the ice age, and now cutting off the centre of the cwm from the outside world.

Clearly this whole boggy central bowl was once a lake, the original seat of the glacier in Cwm Cwyion, but has been almost completely filled in. This is, of course, what must ultimately happen to all glacial lakes – eventually they will be silted up as material eroded higher up the mountain is carried downwards and dumped in the lake. You can spot many places where this process is taking place where 'debris fans' can be seen intruding into a lake.

Cwm Clyd, carved into Y Garn, is both part of the Cwm Idwal complex of cwms, and also part of the row of northern cwms. It is a classic 'armchair' cwm when viewed from below or from the Carneddau. It was created on the boundaries between several different rock types that make up Y Garn, with somewhat softer sedimentary rocks interleaved with different, thin, layers of both the Llewelyn and Snowdon Volcanic Groups, providing weaknesses where ice could accumulate and develop into a glacier. Cwm Clyd also has two small lakes and an obvious filled in patch. It is surrounded by high, steep side and head walls and is another atmospheric, remote cwm cut off from the valley below, indeed its name means 'isolated' in Welsh.

This brings our tour of the northern cwms to an end. As we have seen, the siting of all of them has been determined by geological weaknesses, either the presence of softer rocks or of exploitable rock boundaries. Also, we have seen that the interplay of different rock types has had a considerable effect on the shape of each cwm, the height and steepness of its side and head walls.

Understanding the siting and shaping of these cwms means bringing together much of the story we have followed through this book – tough volcanic rocks interspersed with more or less softer sedimentary rocks; mountain-building exercises that raised and folded the land; and finally the ice that managed to carve incredibly deep trenches and scoops into such tough rocks.

However, before we can turn away from the ice age, we need finally to look at some extraordinary effects of late- and post-glacial times – and what is known as 'periglacial' activity. Our scene moves from the cwms carved into the mountain sides, up to the summits of the Glyderau, and in particular to the summit plateau of Glyder Fawr and Glyder Fach, for here are found some of the oddest rock shapes in central Snowdonia.

I will never forget my first trip to Snowdonia many years ago and, after a gorgeously clear first day on Snowdon, walking the following day in the mist around Tryfan, Glyder Fach, Glyder Fawr and Twll Du. The strange mountains left an even greater impression in the mist than they would have done in clear weather, for the summits were littered with weird rocks – standing upright, angled, or lying flat – forming odd shapes which appeared slowly out of the mist. If the Llanberis Pass is nature's quarry waste tip, then Glyder Fach and Glyder Fawr are nature's Stonehenge.

First, on Glyder Fach, the 'canitilever rock' (see photo w3.5) suddenly appeared, shortly followed by the mad pile of rocks – like some gigantic box of children's toys that has been broken open – that is the summit of Glyder Fach. Then, a bit further on, the shape of 'Castell y Gwynt' (the Castle of the Winds) loomed up in the gloom (see photos 7.8 and w3.6). To me it looks less like a castle than some crazy church or small cathedral, that has perhaps been disturbed by an earthquake and has seen bits fall off, leaving odd spires of rock pointing skywards. It is by far the biggest of the tors, reaching as high as 50 metres above the summit plateau.

Next the route took us across Glyder Fawr. Here the tors are smaller and more subtle, on average just 2.5 metres high, are but much more plentiful in number – about 50 in total on the summit plateau (see photos 7.9 and w3.4). Walking in the mist through this rock and tor field was an unforgettable experience. The two biggest of the tors form Glyder Fawr's twin

Photo 7.8 (top)
Castell y Gwynt,
centre; Snowdon, left;
Glyder Fawr, right.

Photo 7.9 (middle)
Summit plateau, Glyder
Fawr, looking towards
Glyder Fach, showing
'tors' or rock outcrops
created by freeze-thaw
action splitting open
the joints in rocks.

Photo 7.10 bottom)
Winter on Glyder Fach.

summit, though it seems from each as if the other is the actual summit. The path then leads on down to what is one of Snowdonia's most unpleasant descents, a steep scree gully and then to one of its scenic highlights, the exhilarating descent of the Idwal Syncline (Walk 2).

I have been back to these summits many times since, and they never seem to lose their singularly intense character, and which is definitely enhanced by 'bad' weather – mist or snow, for example (see photo 7.10).

Photo 7.11 | Lines of rock created by periglacial processes, Elidir Fawr (best seen lower right).

These weirdly shaped rock outcrops are the product of thousands of years of 'freeze-thaw' cycles through long, cold winters and warmer summers. The constant freezing and thawing of water in joints and cracks in the rocks caused them to split into separate lumps, thus producing the shapes we marvel at today. The process is known to geologists as 'cryofracture'.

Glyder means a 'great pile', in these cases of stones, thus the summit tors give a descriptive name to the whole ridge and its central peaks. The most impressive tors on the Glyderau Ridge are those on Tryfan, Glyder Fach and Glyder Fawr. There are also summit tors on other peaks in the range, though none has the same other-worldly appearance. Elidir Fawr and Carnedd y Filiast have coxcomb summit ridges which have also been created by freeze-thaw, as have the boulder fields which litter other summits, especially Mynydd Perfedd. All these features add considerably to the interest of the Glyderau Ridge, making it, along with the Snowdon massif, one of the best mountain-walking areas in Britain.

Before ending our look at the effect of the ice age on the landscape, it is worth noting briefly a couple of other post-glacial actions which have far less conspicuous effects. On flat surfaces you may note that rocks are sometimes grouped together to form polygonal shapes. This is not accidental, but an action of freeze-thaw at ground level. On some slopes (but certainly not all) the same effect leads to rocks often being sorted into long lines. This is best seen under a light covering of snow, as seen in the photo of such lines on the slopes below the summit of Elidir Fawr (see photo 7.11). These post-glacial effects on the landscape bring us into the time when human beings also became a significant influence.

CHAPTER 8

The Rural Landscape

The landscape – the momentary shape of the earth's surface – is affected by processes in the 'lithosphere', the 'hydrosphere', the 'atmosphere' and the 'biosphere'. We have looked closely at how the geological processes of the lithosphere created igneous rocks and how glacial and 'fluvial' processes of the hydrosphere carved them into shape. In the next two chapters we will look at how the biosphere and, to a lesser extent, the atmosphere are also responsible for what we see when we look at the landscape of Snowdonia.

A few years ago, after a period of very heavy rainfall, several patches of vegetation on the valley slopes of Cwm Brwynog and Cwm Maesgwn were washed away, leaving wide brown/grey gashes. Within a couple of months the gashes were gone, covered with vegetation again, only the slightly more intense green colour gave away their position. This is a fairly common event after heavy rain and is part of the process of erosion that goes on all the time.

Near where the two valleys join, however, there was a much smaller but rather more violent incident. Here a tiny patch of soil and vegetation became dislodged from the steeply-dipping underlying rock. The patch, only about two metres by three metres in area and about one metre deep, must have become loose very suddenly, for it 'wooshed' across the underlying downward dipping rocks, over the lower vegetation, flattening the grass but not carrying it away, then flying over a sharp edge, to become a short-lived mudfall, flowing rapidly down a very steep slope for about 10-15 metres. At the bottom, where the slope becomes much more shallow, there is a footpath next to a stone wall. The fast-moving mass of mud smashed through the stone wall and carried the combined contents another 100 metres before losing its power. Nowadays the only evidence of the event is a slight rise in the land below a gap in the stone wall and slightly different coloured vegetation.

This was a tiny, but still pretty powerful event. Anyone who had been unlucky enough to have been walking along the path at the time would have been killed instantly, smothered in mud, then smashed into and tumbled around in among rocks from the stone wall. But this was a tiny landslip and once you get your eye in you can clearly see the remains of many much larger ones all along the slope.

Further around the valley in Cwm Maesgwn a considerably bigger landslide is evident, though one that probably occurred a few thousand years ago, after the end of the ice age. A large part of the whole mountainside has evidently come sliding down (best seen at a distance from Foel Goch or from within Cwm Maesgwn or in close-up by walking along the edge of the slope between Bwlch Maesgwm and the summit of Moel Cynghorion). Its effects would have made the tiny landslip described above seem totally insignificant in comparison – but neither slip is really of any importance on the wider geological scale. Unless we are unfortunate enough to live in a tectonically active area we are, in these regions, sheltered from major geological activity, for the time being at least. One day the Atlantic Ocean may begin to shrink and the ancient fault systems of North Wales may once again be the site of volcanic activity.

However, the processes of landscape change – weathering, erosion, and the effects of plants and of humans – are taking place on different timescales, even as we observe this seemingly immutable and solid landscape. The landscapes of Snowdonia are in fact ever-changing – and we are part of the process. Human-induced climate change, for example, may increase the scale of erosion by creating more heavy storms – the rate of erosion being linked to the frequency of heavy periods of rain, not just to total volume of rainfall, thus we are likely to see events like those described above much more frequently.

Rocks are also decaying, through the process of 'weathering', even as you look at them. This is due to chemical processes that take place when rock is exposed to air. This is, of course, a very slow process. Weathering also adds to the difficulties of identifying rock types, as it tends to turn most rocks to some shade of grey in colour, thus they loose their distinctive identity. Again, the rate of weathering is related to climate – hot and humid climes lead to faster weathering than hot and dry ones for example.

The biosphere provides another factor which contributes to the breakdown of rocks (and to the difficulty of identifying them), namely lichen. Lichen is a symbiotic organism, combining a fungus and an alga, and with a result that looks completely different from either. Lichens are the first living organisms to colonise mountain areas and, after weathering, are early contributors to the ultimate erosion of rock. There are hundreds of different types of lichens – some types prefer particular rock types, so in such cases they can help with rock identification. In general rock is smothered with a lamination of lichen that prevents you seeing the details of the underlying rock. What may look like a volcanic breccia from a medium distance often turns out to be a lichen-encrusted rock when you get closer to it.

The relationship between rock type and lichen species is complex. One of the most common lichens on both rhyolitic rocks and on slate is the yellow Rhizocarpon species, often

Photo 8.1
'Map' (yellow)
and other lichen.

Photo 8.2
Lichen on
Bedded Pyroclast
Formation rock.

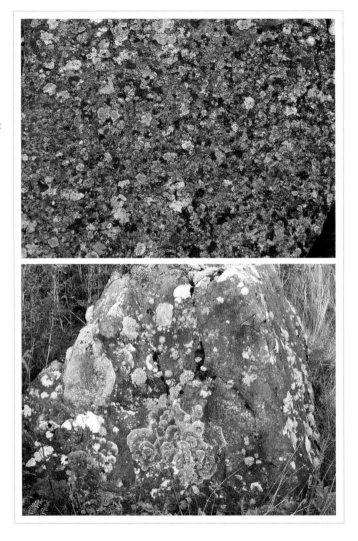

known as 'map lichen' for its resemblance to the way old maps used to distinguish counties (see photo 8.1). It prefers sunny slopes and is completely absent from many north-facing slopes – for example the cliffs of Cwm du'r Arddu. Dolerites and basalts (darker rocks) usually have more species of lichen growing on them than the (lighter) rhyolitic rocks. The Bedded Pyroclastic Formation rocks (generally basaltic), which form rocks shortly below the summit of Snowdon, are particularly rich in lichen, especially in Cwm Glas and on Clogwyn y Garnedd on Snowdon (see photo 8.2).

Lichens are usually easy to see on rocks, but as well as the large, visible varieties, there are also many 'micro-lichens', which can often only be seen with a hand lens. It's worth looking at rocks with such a lens (if one is to hand) to see the amazing shapes taken by these micro-lichens – a whole other miniature world. These micro-lichens are said to be responsible for making rocks slippery. Some 500 different species of lichen have been identified in Snowdonia.

Evidence of the first proper plants to re-appear in the Nant Peris area after the end of the ice age dates back to 10,000 years ago. From then until about 9,000 years ago only the hardiest of plants could survive in the cold climate. The period from about 9,000 to 7,000 years ago saw an improvement in temperatures with birch, pine and hazel trees the first to establish a presence.

Between 7,000 and 5,000 years ago the climate became much wetter. One consequence was that the valley floors turned in many places into boggy mires, but oak and lime trees also took root. From 5,000 to 2,800 years ago there was another warm and dry period followed from 2,800 years ago until today by another wetter phase.

While the trees were establishing themselves, another influence was starting to remove them – human beings. From about 5,000 years ago trees were being cut down by the area's inhabitants and, by 1,000 years ago, all the valleys had been cleared of trees. In his *History of Wales* John Davies describes upland Wales as 'a derelict landscape' because of this deforestation and its ecological consequences for the soil.

In our area trees almost certainly only occupied the valleys and lower slopes. It is estimated that the tree line was as high as 800 metres in the warmer period, with sub-alpine heaths and grassland above that height, although the very highest land experienced arctic-alpine conditions at that time, supporting arctic-alpine plants.

Since 2,800 years ago, the natural tree line has come down to about 470 metres. Or to be more precise, that is where it would be, were it not for the ubiquitous grazing by sheep.

Geology does have an effect on the type of plants that grow in the area. Sometimes indeed you can see where a geological boundary must lie because the plants are suddenly different. Lime-rich rocks lead to more profuse vegetation than acid rocks. Dolerites and 'pyroclastic schists', from the 'Bedded Pyroclastic Formation', support a variety of plant types and provide habitats for rare plants, such as purple saxifrage which can be found in quite surprising quantities in some of the remoter, higher places.

On the other hand rhyolites produce soils that are poor in the diversity of species, nearly all the plants being those that have adapted to grow on lime-free soils – such as heather, bilberry, mat grass, purple moor grass and cotton grass. Much of the soil of central Snowdonia

Photo 8.3 | Standing stone, northern end of Cefn Du (Elidir Fawr, centre distance).

is acid, with only a few areas with better soil. The poor soil is made more so by the heavy rainfall the area experiences and which washes away minerals beyond the reach of plants.

The mountains and the surrounding lower land have long been inhabited and visited. The cairns which mark the summit of mountains such as Y Garn, Elidir Fawr (older name, Garnedd Elidir), Carnedd y Cribau, as well as Carnedd Dafydd and Carnedd Llewelyn (both medieval figures), and many lower cairns, stone circles, hill forts and hut circles, all testify to pre-historic inhabitation of the area. Two of the recommended walks include visits to such archaeological features: on Walk 7 a low-lying ancient cairn on the flanks of Carnedd Cribau, and on Walk 10b to a 'cairn circle', hut circles and a standing stone, on the northern end of Cefn Du (see photos 8.3 and w7.1).

During the later Bronze Age, if not earlier, stone axes were fashioned from the hard volcanic rocks found near Penmaenmawr on the Carneddau. Axes from here have been found in several places across Britain, the start of a long tradition of exploiting the rocks of the area.

Copper was mined extensively on the Great Orme at Llandudno from the Bronze Age. Some 15 kilometres of tunnels were dug to as deep as 70 metres underground. Some 250,000 tons of waste, hauled out by the miners, and dating from between 1,600 and 1,200 BC, is spread around the mines. Around 33,000 bone tools and 2,400 stone hammers have been found so far by archaeologists exploring the site.

The historical evidence of people in the area (in strict terms of history as written evidence) only starts with the Roman period and the writings of Tacitus. It was Tacitus who brought into the world of history the names of the North and South Wales 'tribes' of, respectively, the Ordovices and the Silures. These names were later borrowed by nineteenth-century geologists as the labels for the main geological eras during which the rocks of North and Mid Wales were laid down, the Ordovician and the Silurian (the Cambrian and the Carboniferous periods were also named for their Welsh connections, the former being the Latin name for Wales and the latter referring to the coalfields of South Wales). The Welsh names used for these eras were chosen as much of the original work done in determining the different periods was carried out in Wales, surveying and analysing the rocks.

The Romans left their mark on the landscape with roads (Sarn Helen passes near our area) and forts (around the present-day Pen y Gwryd Hotel, for example).

It is some several centuries before written evidence of our area again becomes available. The collection of ancient British legends, now known as the Mabinogi, is of interest (according to strict academic definitions the Mabinogi refers to only a few specific legends, but common usage applies the name to a wider set of stories). The stories were traditionally communicated orally (and thus subject to change) and were first written down in the medieval period. They thus represent a complex mix of the recent and the ancient, the actual and the imagined, the natural and the supernatural.

Although the stories probably represent people from the early medieval period, one story in particular shows how deep a few of the roots of the legends may stretch. It refers to how it had once been possible to walk from present-day Wales to present-day Ireland. Scientists now calculate that the Irish Sea came into existence about 10,000 years ago at the end of the Ice Age, as glacial melt waters caused sea level to rise (and the English Channel separating England from France came into being a bit later at about 7,000 years of age). For many years before the sea finally covered the land, the area between Wales and Ireland would indeed have been passable, if increasingly wet and tidal.

It seems quite possible that this part of one of the tales is a folk memory of the days before the Irish Sea developed to such an extent that only ships could cross between these Celtic realms.

The post-Roman era itself is mired in myth and legend. It is widely believed that the legendary King Arthur may have been a 'West Briton' and that the name of Bwlch y Saethau (the col of the arrows), below Snowdon's summit, derived from a battle between Saxon invaders and Arthur's followers. Arrowheads have been found here, providing some hard archaeological evidence, but of what, it is more difficult to say. Legend has it that Arthur's warriors, following defeat in the battle, took refuge in a cave in the cliffs of Y Lliwedd, there to await a recall.

Another related legend applies to the hill-fort of Dinas Emrys in Nant Gwynant (see photo 8.4). In AD 796 a British cleric, Nennius, wrote a mythical history of the British people. Some time around AD 430, he says, the British 'travelled far and wide, [until] they came at length to a province called Guenet [Gwynedd]; and having surveyed the mountains of Heremus [Eryri], they discovered on the summit of one of them, a situation, adapted to the construction of a citadel.' Here Emrys, better known as Merlin, was supposed to have been born.

There is general agreement among historians that the place is in fact Dinas Emrys in the Gwynant valley, today still a highly atmospheric place. A narrow ridge connects the hilltop fort with land behind it. Today this vulnerable site is covered by trees and it is hard to appreciate what it would have looked like hundreds of years ago. However, according to archaeologists, it is one of only five hill-forts in Wales that are known to have been in occupation in the early medieval period (400-700 AD), a conclusion based on finds of imported pottery, Germanic glass and ornamental metalwork.

There are other archaeological remains from the medieval era in our area. There are two small royal hafodau buildings (summer residences) in Cwm Brwynog and several medieval boundary ditches around (for example, on the northern ridge of Moel Eilio, in Cwm Perfedd in the northern Glyderau, and on the bwlch between Carnedd y Cribau and Moel Meirch).

Though there was more crop-growing in upland Wales than nowadays, the agriculture of the mountains of Snowdonia was primarily pastoral. 'Transhumance' was the standard, but with cattle and goats rather than sheep, moving in summer to the 'Hafod' or summer hut (summer in Welsh = haf). Any worthwhile land was farmed, and settlement of the lower slopes of the mountains was far more intense than is generally imagined.

Over the millennia agriculture underwent only minor changes (and then generally in response to changing climatic conditions) until the high medieval period. Before then, and

Photo 8.4 | Dinas Emrys.

stretching back to pre-history, the same fields and the same settlements were used and re-used according to the latest archaeological findings.

The expansive dynamic of European feudal civilization brought about far-reaching changes. After Edward I defeated Llewelyn ap Gruffydd in 1281, the Welsh prince's lands in Gwynedd, west of the river Conwy and on Anglesey, came under the direct control of the king as his personal lands. A Justice of North Wales, based at Caernarfon, was appointed to administer the area. The ring of castles (Beaumaris, Conwy, Caernarfon, Harlech) was built around the mountain fastnesses to prevent further resurgence of local power and the smaller

Welsh castles (in our area, Dolbadarn at Llanberis where Llewelyn had imprisoned his older brother for over 20 years) were put out of use.

Snowdonia became a royal hunting 'forest'. This is often interpreted to mean that a lot of trees must have been removed since medieval times; but this is a misapprehension. 'Forest' used to mean a royal hunting area, not an area of extensive woodland as we now use the term. The post of the Forester of Snowdon was not given to a tree-feller, but to the keeper of 'the stags of Snowdon'.

The Pig Track possibly gets its name from this historic function of the area. Bwlch Moch, where the climb up to Crib Goch leaves the Pig Track, is usually translated as the 'pass of the pigs'. But some writers suggest that a better translation is the 'pass of the swine' and that it originates from the hunting chase of wild animals through the forest in medieval times. An alternative view is that it should really be called the Pyg Track after Pen y Gwryd. I will leave it to the reader to decide which version they prefer.

It is difficult to estimate the population of Snowdonia during the high medieval period, but it was possibly lower than before as regal policy was aimed at reducing the number of inhabitants of forests. However, there is some evidence that the upland areas of Wales in general were soon to become more heavily populated and in the high medieval period (about 1150 to 1250) there was considerable population growth, in part due to climatic improvement, and consequent pressure on land use patterns of the upland areas.

If the feudal knights and their armies represented the cutting edge of military feudalism, a new breed of churchmen, the Cistercians, represented its ideological and economic leadership. They introduced 'modern' economic practices to their extensive land ownings in Wales, which included a large estate on the southern side on Snowdon, known as Nanhwynain (Nant Gwynant).

It was the Cistercians who first introduced sheep to Wales in large numbers, especially on their upland lands, such as Nanhwynain whose boundaries stretch to the ridge line of the low mountain range to the south-east of Snowdon, from Carnedd y Cribau to Mynydd Sygun (see photo w7.8). The Cistercians' agricultural practices often had profound effects on the landscape of their estates with extensive drainage alterations, reclamations and new patterns of use. In our area, the introduction of widespread sheep grazing (starting from Cistercian times) led to compacting of the soil and increased run off, as well as reduced bio-diversity.

Agriculture in North Wales started to undergo far-reaching changes beginning in Tudor times. During the reign of Elizabeth I, on the eve of Britain's transition to being the spearhead of the modern commercial and industrial world, a 'spy' was commissioned to learn what he could about the religious life of Wales. In his report, now in a batch of manuscripts relating to Wales and held at the British Museum in London, the spy reported on what he had seen in western Snowdonia: 'Upon Sundays and holidays the multitude of all sorts meet in sundry places either on some hill or on the side of some mountain where their harpers and fiddlers sing them songs of the doings of their ancestors.'

Perhaps the tales that were listened to on those hills and mountainsides were derived from those written down in the Mabinogi. The landscape of Wales at the dawn of the modern era was little different from that celebrated in the Mabinogi. Apart, that is, from the appearance of dense flocks of Cistercian sheep and highly conspicuous Edwardian castles – precursors of far-reaching changes that would be wrought by industrial age on the landscapes of Snowdonia.

Photo 8.5

Sheep have been reared on these slopes since medieval times.

CHAPTER 9

The Industrial Landscape

Far-reaching change, caused by human beings, began to affect the landscape of central Snowdonia from the beginning of the nineteenth century. The system of enclosures came late to Wales in general and even later to remote areas such as Eryri, which remained largely unaffected until the time of the Napoleonic Wars when sheep farming underwent further expansion (see photo 8.5).

Economic historian, A H Dodd, wrote that, 'vast stretches of mountain pasture and extensive marshy wastes ... formed the main objective of the apostles of enclosure. Common rights in the village fields were extinguished by a silent and gradual process ... The mountain pastures were to have a much stormier history. ... So long as the waste lands remained unimportant, ownership was left conveniently vague, but when suddenly they rose to the rank of national asset, the community was rudely awakened ... At a time when war conditions called for every ounce of foodstuffs the land could bear, the Welsh pastures were certainly failing 'to do their bit' ... In 1802 the first assault was made on the rocky wastes of the Lleyn Peninsula, which became the scene of extensive enclosures during the next ten years. The marsh of Dinas Dinlle, south-west of Caernarfon, was enclosed and drained under an act of 1806; in the same year the northern spurs of Snowdon were attacked.'

This is the period during which the stone walls started to rise up and crisscross the mountainsides, demarking the land of one owner from that of another. The national enclosure movement, however, was already losing momentum by the time the mountains came under attack and its effects were limited to lower slopes.

Much of the road network of central Snowdonia also dates from the beginning of the nineteenth century and the construction of 'turnpikes'. The road from Capel Curig to Bangor was completed in 1802 (with the primary purpose of improving the journey for travellers to Ireland). The roads between Capel Curig, via Pen y Pass, and Llanberis, and between Caernarfon and Aberglaslyn, followed soon after.

These roads, however, although intended to provide for through traffic, soon were thronged with a new type of traveller in North Wales, the tourist seeking out the delights and horrors of the frightful mountainous landscape. The earlier generations of visitors had

Photo 9.1 | Snowdon Mountain Railway.

tended to be men of science – botanists and geologists describing the landscape and its natural history, including such intellectual giants as Charles Darwin who, after seeing glaciers in South America, realised that the scenery he saw before him in Cwm Idwal had clearly been carved out during an ice age. Their work popularised mountainous areas, and as there was a long-standing hill-walking tradition in the area, so the mountains started to attract many more tourists.

Later on, that icon of the industrial age, the steam railway, brought many more visitors to North Wales and eventually steam and iron rails even took them up all the up to the summit of Snowdon itself, on the mountain railway (see photo 9.1). Tourism was one of two industries on and around Snowdon, which really grew in parallel during the nineteenth century – the other being slate quarrying.

Slate had been used locally for several centuries, but the industry really took off in the industrial age. The northern ends of both Nant Ffrancon and the Llanberis Pass are notable for their massive slate waste tips. In the case of the Dinorwig quarry in Llanberis, the tips rise well over half-way up the mountain side – and as the mountain in question, Elidir Fawr, is over 900 metres high, the slate tips dominate the view of the mountain from Llanberis (at 100 metres above sea level), with the highest workings at over 600 metres. See photos 9.2 and 9.3.

Present convention would see our area and its lower lying surrounding land as a mountain-cum-rural landscape. But from the end of the eighteenth century until the mid-twentieth the areas around Llanberis, Bethesda and the Gwyrfai and Nantlle valleys to the west were industrial landscapes – stone walls marking enclosure, roads and railways intro-ducing previously unknown mobility, and industrial quarry technology supporting extraction on an ever more gigantic scale.

Photo 9.2 |
Dinorwig slate quarry.

Photo 9.3 |
Dinorwig slate
quarry view.

The silent waste tips we see today would have been busy places, with many small steam locos noisily hauling the wagons of waste back and forth. Llyn Padarn's two railways would have been busy too, the locos hauling wagons filled with the valuable slate to the quarry company's own docks 15 kilometres away at Port Dinorwig (Y Felinheli) on the Menai Strait or to Caernarfon.

The quarries also used 'inclines' or 'inclined planes' to lower the good slate to the railhead. There are two massive inclines visible in the Dinorwig quarry (and a smaller, partly restored one in the National Slate Museum grounds next door which shows what they would have looked like in their prime – Walk 13).

The quarries at the northern end of the Snowdon massif are the biggest, but there are plenty of other quarry remains on Snowdon, including several small trial workings that can be encountered at odd spots (see photo 9.4).

Photo 9.4 | Trial quarry (near Bwlch Cwm Brwynog).

Photo 9.5 | Dangerous section on public footpath to Nant Peris.

Photo 9.6 | Abandoned 'caban' in Dinorwig slate quarry.

Photo 9.7 | Abandoned slate workshop in Dinorwig slate quarry.

If you do explore the quarries remember to take very great care. The faces and some waste tips are unstable and you could easily fall victim to an accident if you enter the quarries. Even the public footpaths are not wholly safe in quarry territory (see photo 9.5).

Including those in Blaenau Ffestiniog and Corris, there are over 60 quarries in North Wales which, at their height, employed over 18,000 people. The area saw the growth of a distinct modern, Welsh-speaking, non-conformist culture. The quarry workers developed their own cultural activities in their 'caban' or cabin. There is an abandoned caban high up in Dinorwig quarry where some old jackets and shoes were discarded when the quarry was closed in the 1960s (see photo 9.7). Elsewhere, among the ruins of power sheds and incline brake houses, and there are the rows of barracks where men who did not live locally stayed during the working week. One barracks can be seen in the National Slate Museum grounds (Walk 1). 'Barics Môn', the Anglesey Barracks, was used by quarrymen from the island.

The industrial remains are plentiful too. High up there's an old saw mill (long and narrow to fit on to the ledge created by a waste tip) with rusting machines and a collapsing roof (see photo 9.7). There are also odd remains such as ladders attached to vertical quarry faces which the quarrymen would have used, and parts of the overhead haulage systems that were used to raise slate and waste from the quarry workings. Most impressive of all are the massive holes which the quarryworkers dug in order to get at the slate.

The remains of quarrying are not all so conspicuous as the pits and tips, and there are many more subtle effects which may be noted – many mountain lakes, for example, were dammed to increase their level and thus their usefulness in powering machinery in slate quarries further down the hill. You can stumble across leats that run horizontally across a hillside collecting water, the remains of old dams, and even, in Cwm Llan, the sunken remains of old reservoirs. These can be navigational hazards (or, to the alert walker and map reader, navigational aids) as well as items of interest on any walk. Also look out for the fences, bridges, gate posts and even stiles made out of slate in many mountain areas.

Although a lot of quarry workers and their families lived in local villages, many also lived on smallholdings. There's a very distinctive feature marked on OS maps north-west of Bethesda, at Mynydd Llandegai. Rows of straight lines mark extremely large 'gardens' attached to quarryworkers' houses.

Similarly, in the area behind Llanberis and below Cwm Dwythwch, there are well over 20 ruins. Near Hebron station, where the public footpath to Helfa Fawr leaves the tarmac track, there's also the remains of the community's church – now behind metal barriers to prevent the inquisitive from becoming victims of the parlous condition of the building. Indeed, Hebron station was put in place to serve the local community. Several footpaths crisscross the area, from which the remains of old cottages can be seen. At first glance one sees only a handful of ruins, but soon the full extent of habitation in this area becomes clear. This area and others were abandoned in the 1950s and 1960s, as the slate industry declined and people moved increasingly into the 'slate villages' such as Llanberis and Deiniolen.

Another area of abandoned settlements is found behind the low ridge on the north-eastern side of Llyn Padarn, with an intricate set of walled paths connecting the forgotten cottages (Walk 10a).

Slate is certainly the most conspicuous, but is not the only produce harvested from the geological heritage of the area. Snowdon in particular is also marked by several copper

Photo 9.8

Cwm Maesgwn.

and mineral mines: opposite Nant Peris, in Cwm du'r Arddu, Glaslyn, Cwm Merch (below Y Lliwedd), Hafod y Llan, Braichyroen, Hafod y Porth and Pantku.

There's also a cluster of copper mines near Cwm Ceunant on the Glyderau Ridge and several related mines occur to the south of Snowdon (see photo 9.9), including the Sygun Copper Mine which is now a museum and offers underground tours of the old mine shafts.

A word of warning; these old mineral mines can be even more dangerous than the generally more conspicuous slate quarries. Some copper mines are no more than gashes in the earth and may not be seen until you are right up to them (see photo 9.10). In recent years some of the gashes of the Glaslyn copper mines (Brittannia) just below the Pig Track have been fenced off to prevent accidents, but some remain.

The main feature giving away the presence of a mineral mine is usually a brown coloured waste tip seen on some hillside (see photo 9.9). Close examination of the hill near the tip may reveal a gash which marked the entrance to the miners' place of work.

Photo 9.9 | Copper mines, Mynydd Sygun.

Photo 9.10 | Unguarded copper mine entrance, Crafnant area.

One of the most common small-scale features of the landscape of central Snowdonia is quartz. This glassy rock, usually white, can be seen in seams in many places. Some seams – for instance in the Cambrian Carnedd y Filiast Grits – form intricate networks within the host rock. At other places it forms really quite thick veins – some very impressive such veins can be seen from the Pig and the Miners' Tracks near Llyn Lladaw. The day I wrote these words I went for a walk near Pen y Pass, into Cwm Beudy Mawr above the Llanberis Pass. There I came across some substantial quartz veins – two or three metres wide. Then I noticed that there were a series of veins going down the hillside, getting narrower lower down, and that each vein formed the top or bottom of a small crag. One of the narrower veins towards the base of the hillside, where I sat for a cup of tea and a biscuit, ran across the path of a minor stream, forming a tiny waterfall (see photo 9.11), a vein of tough quartz in only slightly less tough volcanic tuffs. In fact it appeared, looking back up, that the quartz veins played an important part in the shaping of the hillside, when it was carved out by the outlet glacier that breached Pen y Pass and flowed down towards Anglesey.

White quartz is the commonest mineral intrusion into the rocks of our area. Rather less common is coloured quartz, though you can see lumps of yellow-brown or reddish-brown quartz in several places on the hills. The discolouring is caused by the presence of other minerals in the hot liquids. Some of the most intensely coloured quartz is found close to copper mines, where it has been mixed up with the rarer minerals, creating copper and other metals.

'Mineralisation', the process of intrusion of these liquids and subsequent creation of minerals, took place mainly in the Bedded Pyroclastic Formation rocks, near the boundary with the earlier Lower Rhyolitic Tuffs at a depth of about 1-2 kilometres and probably within about 5-15 million years after the Snowdon Caldera collapsed. Much of the metallic mineral content is believed to have leached out of previously intruded volcanic rocks at high levels in the earth's crust, as 'hydrothermal' cells rose upwards powered by the last embers of the molten magma. Minerals may also have been present in the original magma.

The copper mines on Snowdon and near to it, although apparently scattered across the massif, are in fact grouped mainly around the line running roughly north-east to south-west. The Cwm du'r Arddu mine is on the line of the great Snowdon syncline and the Idwal-Hebog fault zone. The copper mines near Nant Peris occur in sedimentary rocks from well before the volcanic era, but are associated with the intensely folded strata in that area.

Swansea, in South Wales, was the centre of the metals industry in the eighteenth and nineteenth century and the earliest written records of Snowdon copper come from Swansea in 1804. The Britannia mine in Glaslyn produced ore intermittently from 1889 to 1915. Some remains of the Britannia mine can be safely examined from the hollow of Upper Glaslyn, off the Pig Track (with great care of course as there are open mine shafts around here). Among the detritus you can find lumps of purple quartz and many other coloured rocks, as well as fragments of metallic minerals.

The mine also played a part in establishing the network of tracks which climb up the mountain. The Miners' Track has an obvious origin, but the Snowdon Ranger's track preceded it as the route on which copper was carried down (to Llyn Cwellyn where it was then transported to Caernarfon). These and other foot tracks, and also the later mountain railway track, make very conspicuous marks on the mountain, but enable hundreds of thousands of people a year to visit the summit of Snowdon and to appreciate it in their own ways. Indeed, we should really include the massed crowds of people who surround the summit cairn on sunny days as part of the landscape.

The national park authorities and other agencies do really excellent work in maintaining and improving the tracks. Their work has led to paths that are capable of supporting those hundreds of thousands of pairs of boots tramping up and down them in all weathers. Before the Pig Track was improved in the 1980s it suffered badly from widespread erosion, leaving great scars as a mark on the landscape – and providing weak points for rainwater to speed up the overall rate of erosion. Since the improvements the situation has fully recovered.

Water and height are the main factors in another primary industry that has a fairly conspicuous effect on the landscape – energy production from water. The pipeline that runs from Llyn Llydaw to the Gwynant valley feeds a hydraulic power station. A campaign to have the pipeline put underground was unsuccessful and it remains a key intrusive feature of the landscape in this masterpiece of natural glacial sculpture (see photo 9.12).

Less intrusive is the power station in the old Dinorwig quarry, but only because the quarry remains overpower the power station buildings and much of it is housed in a massive cavern dug into the mountain. A plunge pool, surrounded by an electric fence, sits at around 650 metres, above even the highest quarry workings, but it is still comparatively inconspicuous.

There are many other aspects of human influence on the landscape, too many really to be covered in a short book like this. The automobile, for example, lies behind enormous shifts in the patterns of habitation, work and tourism. Constant flows of moving traffic and, especially on weekends, long lines of parked cars are now an intrinsic part of the landscape, for better or for worse (see photo 9.13). The problem is that, just as we can't really see the tiny cumulative changes to the landscape, we don't really notice that the lines of cars get longer each year.

My 1983 copy of W. A. Poucher's classic route guide, The Welsh Peaks, refers to the ease of parking at Pen y Pass with extra capacity provided at its 'large car park'. Now even the

Photo 9.11 (left) | Quartz vein.

Photo 9.12 (top right) | Intrusive hydroelectric pipeline, Cwm Dyli, Snowdon horseshoe.

Photo 9.13 (bottom) | An ever more obvious feature of the modern landscape.

enlarged car park is much too small to meet an insatiable demand. It is often full before 9 a.m. at weekends and there is pressure for more parking spaces to be provided on and around Snowdon and the Glyderau. We can only be dimly aware of the subtle, cumulative changes that the automobile and modern patterns of life are bringing in their wake.

At the time of writing this book, the 'café' on the summit of Snowdon has been demolished (see photo 9.14), to be replaced by a new building. The large ancient cairn that used to stand on the summit was demolished two centuries ago and a succession of buildings has been erected and then demolished in its place on the very top of this wonderful mountain and it is now almost impossible to imagine it without some sort of building on its topmost reaches, nor indeed without its chugging train (the experience of ascending the rocky wilderness of the Pig Track to arrive at Bwlch Glas, only to be greeted by a puffing stream engine is too weird to put in words). And of course there are many other buildings halfway up the

Photo 9.14 | A fleeting glimpse – Snowdon's summit without a building in the winter of 2006/2007, after the old building had been demolished and before work started on the new one.

mountain – mainly quarry and mining ruins, but also sheep folds and a modern café (the Halfway House).

Having looked briefly at human effects on the landscape, it is time to bring this section of the book on the landscapes of Snowdonia to an end. I hope that this account of the factors which have affected the landscape will enhance the reader's appreciation of and interest to be gained from walking that landscape. I have tried to concentrate on the land that you can see in front of you and hope that the information provided helps the reader to see and understand more of the landscape. But let's not forget that 'landscape' as such is an entirely human construct, about how we view and interpret the world around us and our place in it.

About the Walks

Two factors have been central to selecting the walks – quality of views and geological/geomorphological interest. I have arranged the walks in three groups to ensure a wide range of different areas, aspects and degrees of effort.

First, I describe some of the features that can be seen on several of the major walking routes on Snowdon, the Glyderau and the Carneddau (Walks 1, 2, 3, 4 and 5) . These may suit the walker, perhaps making a first trip to the area, who wants to see the highlights and climb the major peaks rather than follow a 'geology trail'.

Second, there are some walks that go off the trodden tracks to visit remoter areas of central Snowdonia where some of the more hidden geological wonders can be examined. These walks are aimed at the walker who has already climbed the main peaks and wants to deepen their acquaintance with the area. Some of these walks are tough, potentially dangerous routes in remote, crag-ridden areas, and require good navigational skills. They are thus aimed at more experienced hillwalkers, though there is also one fairly easy walk in this section too (Walks 6, 7, 8 and 9).

Third, there are some low level walks for days when, even if it's not raining, cloud obscures the summits. Landscape is very much about views, and cloud and mist rob the walker of those views (though they can usefully concentrate the attention on the 'micro-landscape'). The low level walks offer some options for cloudy or wet days and, unless the cloud comes down uncommonly low, still give good views. These walks range from fairly straightforward to very hard going – the latter just like a mountain walk, but at low level. They are designed to explore a different perspective on the scale of mountain landscape (Walks 10, 11, 12 and 13).

The sketch maps for the walks are designed to show the general route and are for use in conjunction with the OS 1:25,000 map (OL17). They are very emphatically not designed to be sufficient to use on their own as it is impossible to show the precise route with sufficient accuracy. It is thus essential, before going out on the mountains, to plan the route on the OS map and to take the map for use when out walking. Grid references are given as 6 or 8 figures as appropriate; most, but not all, have been verified using GPS. All grid references are in the SH area so it hasn't been necessary to add this to each reference. However, one point to keep an eye on is that the both the 'eastings' and 'northings' 60 grid lines cross in the middle of our area (in the middle of some waste tips in the Dinorwig Quarry). This means that extra care should be taken to read grid references in the correct order, starting with reading the first set of numbers going across the map to identify the correct the vertical line (the 'easting'), and then going up the map to identify the correct horizontal line (the 'northing'). The grid reference for the summit of Snowdon is 609 543. If read the wrong way around (northings first, then eastings) it would point you to very unpleasant terrain on Cefn Du, 10 kilometres to the north.

It will make sense to read the walk description before going on the walk and then to take a photocopy of the relevant pages, or the book itself, along on the walk as a reminder of what to see and where.

To give the reader an idea of how hard a walk might be and what sort of challenges it may pose, I have borrowed (and slightly adapted) a system for ranking the walks from Ralph Storer's book, *100 Best Routes on Scottish Mountains*. This system allows a more nuanced assessment to be given than a vague 'hard' or 'easy'. For each walk I give a ranking on a scale of 1 to 5 (1 – easiest, 5 – hardest) for three areas: navigation, terrain and 'severity'. Even so some arbitrariness must apply. For example a walk may be very easy generally, navigation- or terrain-wise, but still have one or two short but seriously more challenging sections. In such situations I have given the ranking earned by the most difficult section.

A high navigation ranking means that there are places or sections on the route where it would be easy to make an error and head off in the wrong direction or get onto potentially dangerous ground.

A high score for terrain may be due to either having sections of steep ground, the need for some scrambling (i.e. essential use of hands as well as feet to ascend/descend) or it may be due to some very rough going (usually tussocky grass/heather and hidden boulders and holes in the ground).

By severity, I mean the chance for things to go badly wrong in the event of a minor navigation error or a simple accident – so in general the most 'severe' walks are those that go up high, and/or off the popular tracks to remote areas with few other people around.

All the rankings apply to good weather conditions with clear views of the walk. I must recommend that you do not attempt any of the higher level walks in snow and ice, or in tempestuous weather unless you are fully confident that you have the experience and skill to cope with harsh conditions.

I have used some terms in specific ways. In general I have used the term 'track' for any obvious trail on the ground – from a motor-vehicle track to a sheep track, and anything in between. Some tracks are marked on the 1:25,000 OS map by thin dashed black lines, but many more are not marked at all. Terms such as narrow track, wispy track and twisting track are all, I hope, self-explanatory.

By 'footpath' I mean a public right of way marked in green on the OS 1:25,000 map (thus including bridleways). It is important to note that the course of the actual track on the ground may not be the same as the line of the footpath shown in green on the map; this can be confusing if navigating in an unfamiliar area and should be watched out for.

In the directions I use phrases such as 'after about 10 metres of descent' (or ascent) to indicate vertical distance to be travelled and phrases such as 'after another 100 metres or so' to mean horizontal distance. The former will usually apply on steep ground and the latter in less steep areas, though it depends on the specific circumstances – for example, with a gently sloping track diagonally crossing a steep slope, distance would probably be appropriate.

Getting to the walks

I have centred all the walks on Llanberis, Pen y Pass, Pen y Gwryd, Idwal Cottage or Nant Gwynant. Llanberis is a good base for anyone travelling to the area by public transport (train to Bangor, then bus), with a wide range of accommodation, supplies, pubs, cafes and restaurants, and bus services to the mountain areas.

All the walks, except for the main Elidir Fawr route, can be done without use of a car from Llanberis or Idwal Cottage, though sometimes needing the help of buses (and there is an alternative route provided for Elidir Fawr for those without access to a car). Most walks start and end either at main centres or bus stops such as Llanberis, Idwal Cottage, Pen y Gwryd or Pen y Pass. I have done all the walks, or slightly longer versions of them, either on foot from Llanberis or Idwal Cottage, some with the help of buses (although it has usually been a lot easier when using a car).

Car users should be aware that the car park at Pen y Pass is often full even before 9 a.m. on busy Sundays and during the summer school holidays. There are some lay-bys lower down the Pass and, in the other direction, around Pen y Gwryd, but these too fill quickly on busy days. The alternative is to park in a car park in Llanberis, Nant Peris, Bethesda, Capel Curig, Betws y Coed or Beddgelert and use the Sherpa buses.

Using the Sherpa service it is possible to plan linear walks, as well as those described in this book which start and finish at the same point. The bus service has improved a lot from just a few years ago when there were only one or two buses a day in busy tourist areas and it was not unusual for them not to turn up at all. All the same, the service is still poorly organised and operated compared with bus services in continental Europe. Unfortunately, there is no circular service which is what would really be needed for a practical and popular bus network.

Hazards

It is possible, even for experienced walkers, to underestimate the physical demands of walking on the Welsh mountains and of the potential for good weather to turn into threatening conditions, sometimes within a few minutes. Even in midsummer it can feel like winter if you are high up and the cloud, wind and rain descend. So always take spare clothing, water- and wind-proofs, a torch, food and drink, a good quality survival bag (such as those available from 'Blizzard Protection Systems') and a map and compass. And on your feet you need good boots. Check the weather forecast before you go start the walk (available from the Met Office website mountain area forecasts page or notice boards at Pen y Pass and Idwal Cottage).

It may well be possible to go up and down Snowdon without a map – thousands do so every year. But even here things can go wrong if you are not fully orientated and aware of the scale of the mountain landscape.

I once met an exhausted family, well on their way down the Snowdon Ranger path to the Gwyrfai valley, who thought they were heading to Llanberis and their parked car. A fit walker with a knowledge of map-reading could have found a way to get to Llanberis (via Cwm Brwynog or Cwm Maesgwm), but given their state of near collapse they had little choice but to carry on and then get one bus to Caernarfon and another back out to Llanberis, not so easy on a Sunday or in winter when buses are few and far between. A map, a compass and knowledge of how to use them are essential for these walks – even on Snowdon.

Remember that if you go high up you must be prepared to have to navigate your way off the mountain using map and compass alone if, for example, mist should descend suddenly while you are on the summit.

It is very easy indeed to misjudge the scale of features in the mist – a tiny insignificant gully can easily look like a major gorge in restricted visibility. So it is all too easy to go in the wrong direction or onto dangerous ground.

The OS 1:25,000, OL17, map is incredibly good value, covering a considerable area and is an excellent map. The OS 1:50,000 Snowdon or the Harvey 1:40,000 Snowdonia maps are useful for showing the shape of the ground better than the 1:25,000 map where the amount of detail can obscure the contour lines that allow the shape to be interpreted from the map. While that makes them helpful adjuncts, the detail of the OS 1:25,000 map can be vital in restricted visibility, so if you only take one map, make sure it is OL17 (and preferably a waterproof version). Similarly, a GPS device can be a useful adjunct to map and compass, but should not be relied upon on its own.

No skill (apart of course from the actual art of walking) is more important to enjoying the hills safely than map-reading. There are many organisations and qualified instructors based in Snowdonia who arrange courses in the local hills (see www.Snowdonia-Active.com for lists of course providers and much more about walking and other activities in the area).

For the landscape lover, the usual mountain hazards are multiplied. Wandering off to look at rocks, views and so on can add significantly to the time needed for a walk and this should be taken into account, especially in the short days of winter. Thus the times suggested for the recommended walks in this book are somewhat longer than would be given in a general hillwalking guidebook (and include allowances for stopping to explore rocks and features, for contemplation and refreshment, for enjoyment and, hopefully, enlightenment).

Exploring old mines and quarries is particularly dangerous. Do not enter mines, tunnels or holes in the ground. In copper and lead mining areas especially, look out for open holes in the ground down which you could easily fall, never to come back up again! In quarries watch out for unstable rock faces which may, and do, collapse at any time. The same is true for waste tips which can be unstable, especially after heavy rain. Don't get too close to the edge at the top of quarry faces – those little gulleys running parallel to the cliff edge are tension cracks where the rocks are preparing to slip. From below, always look up as you approach a cliff or quarry face to see if there is anything that looks as if it is about to topple on you.

Geology maps and general guides

A geology map Is extremely useful if you want to become more familiar with the different rock types. The British Geological Survey's most up to date 1:25,000 maps cover central Snowdonia, but you would need three of them for the whole area dealt with in this book, at about £10 each. (Classical areas of British Geology 1:25,000 series: Llyn Padarn, 1988; Snowdon, 1989; Passes of Nant Ffrancon and Llanberis, 1985).

However, there is an earlier 1:25,000 map which covers a much bigger area, encompassing most of the Snowdon Volcanic Group rocks (though not the Cambrian sedimentary rocks described in chapter 2 or the Carneddau). Two minor disadvantages are that it is a bit less precise than the later maps and it is not the latest analysis of the grouping of the different outcrops (for example it assigns the Yr Arddu Tuffs to the Pitts Head Tuffs), but these are not serious problems and at about £10 for the sheet it is the best choice for the interested reader. (Special Sheet: Central Snowdonia, 1972).

When buying geology maps always make sure that you specify 'solid' (or on newer maps 'bedrock') and avoid maps with the term 'drift' (or on newer maps 'superficial') on them.

There are also 1:50,000 scale geology maps (Sheet 119, Snowdon; Sheet 106, Bangor), but the detail is much harder to see and the division between the maps is not very useful as it cuts through just above Snowdon.

Bryan Lynas's *Snowdonia Rocky Rambles* (Sigma, 1996) is well worth reading if you can find a copy as it is now out of print. I have devised the recommended walks in this book as much as possible to complement, rather than to repeat, the walks outlined in Lynas's book. I have also tried to minimize any duplication of the walks outlined in the book by M F Howells and others, *Snowdonia: a geological field guide* (Unwin, 1981).

Peter Hermon's two-volume *Hillwalking in Wales* is far and away the best general guide book for hillwalkers in Wales with a vast number of routes up all of Wales's mountains (defined as summits over 2,000 feet). Volume two covers the Glyderau and Snowdon, as well as many other ranges, but not the Carneddau which is in volume one.

W A Poucher's *The Welsh Peaks* deals with all the main ranges of central Snowdonia, but has only a fraction of the total number of routes covered by Hermon. However, Poucher has excellent photos, many with the routes marked on them to help with planning – and with navigation while out if you carry it with you.

As matters on the ground can change – stiles for example can be moved or new fences can appear – some of the information about the walks may become out of date. I will try to post update details if or when I become aware of them on the website www.rock-trails.co.uk where readers can also contact me to inform me of errors and changes.

Entreaty

Please take note of the Countryside Code – the most important injunctions are to close gates and leave absolutely no litter. Snowdonia is a national park, and strictly speaking one shouldn't even remove already loose fossils or rock samples. There is certainly no justification for trying to lever or smash them out of rock outcrops. For everyone, the main thing is to use common sense in minimising the impact you have on the environment.

Snowdon

Snowdon – Yr Wyddfa – is not only the highest peak in Wales, but fittingly it's also the visually most magnificent and the scenically most compelling. From our point of view it is also the geologically most interesting of mountains. Here you traipse up and down a vast variety of types of volcanic rock (including some of the thickest formations of all of the volcanic period in Snowdonia), and you encounter a variety of geological features, as well as having your senses engaged by the exaggeratedly intense glacial sculpting of the rock.

A trip to the summit, if possible on a clear day, is an essential part of any visit to Snowdonia and is equally vital to appreciating the full majesty of its superb scenery.

Without doubt the best of the main routes up and down Snowdon are those from Pen y Pass. This is because of the scenic drama of the Snowdon Horseshoe and not just because, standing at 365 metres, Pen y Pass is the highest starting point for a climb to the summit of Yr Wyddfa at 1085 metres. Of course, it should not be thought that any of the other main routes are scenically uninteresting; indeed all are superb in their own way, each showing a quite different aspect of this magnificent mountain.

There are four main routes from Pen y Pass to the summit, all of them utterly wonderful. The tough bit is choosing which of them to use.

The classic horseshoe route is over the knife-edge ridge of Crib Goch, via Crib y Ddysgyl, to the summit of Snowdon, then descending via Y Lliwedd. This is certainly a memorable day's walking and scrambling – indeed it is among the best mountain scrambles in Britain. The view of the horseshoe from the start of the Crib Goch Ridge is unforgettable (see photo 6.14). However, the Crib Goch section is demanding of one hundred percent attention and a fairly cool head, for there are some pretty big drops and this route will not suit all hillwalkers, especially if you want to linger and study the rocks and landscape. Quite big queues can build up for the crossing during busy periods and result in pressure to keep moving. Even though thousands make a safe crossing every year, the ridge takes its toll (indeed I read in the week before completing this book of one man who fell to his death from Crib Goch while out walking with his son-in-law).

So, given that the walks are intended to allow time and opportunity to observe the landscape, my recommended route for visiting the summit of Snowdon is intended to give excellent views and slightly easier walking using the popular tracks the Miners' track, the Pig track and the track over Y Lliwedd (Walk 1).

The Snowdon massif is quite big and it has a wide variety of aspects. The rocky magnificence of the horseshoe is only one such aspect and the walker will do well to explore other parts of the mountain if time is available. I have also included elsewhere two more walks on the Snowdon massif which can begin to introduce the walker to the wider and subtler charms of Yr Wyddfa (Walk 9 on the southern flank and Walk 12 in Cwm Dwythwch on the northern arm of the massif).

I did consider including some walks within some of Snowdon's less frequented cwms such as Cwm Glas, Cwm du'r Arddu and Cwm Clogwyn. However, these are frequently trackless, requiring of scrambling, often very craggy (Cwm Glas especially) and quite remote if something should go wrong. To enjoy this type of walking you need to be sufficiently independent and navigationally skilled. If this interests you, do explore these areas using what you have picked up from this book in looking out for recognizable features, for there are indeed some amazing rocks and geological features to be seen. But, do take care and be aware of your own limits.

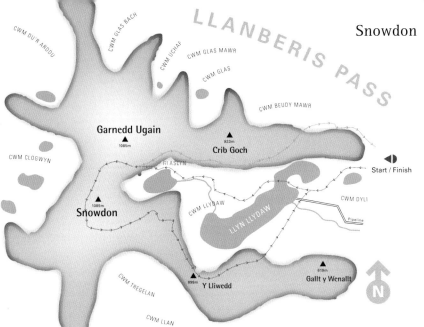

Walk #1 Snowdon

START	▶	PEN Y PASS (647 556) OR PEN Y GWRYD (6610 5595)
FINISH	●	CIRCULAR ROUTE
TIME	☻	6 HOURS+
GRADE	❶	NAVIGATION ● ● ●
	☁	TERRAIN ● ● ● ●
	❸	SEVERITY ● ● ● ● (DUE TO LENGTH AND REMOTENESS)

As the car park at Pen y Pass can become full quite early in the day (especially at weekends and in summer) it may make sense to use the Sherpa bus service.

The recommended ascent makes use of the fairly easy Miners' Track – easy for its first half anyway, followed by a stiff climb on a good track. It offers a relaxed start to the walk, taking you into the jaws of the glacial cwms, where the mountain roars up above you all around, conveying the sense of size of the glaciers which once flowed down here.

The Miners' Track merges in its second half with the Pig Track and climbs up to Bwlch Glas and the ridge leading to the summit. Throughout this section the views of the horseshoe are excellent.

There are two options for the descent. If you have the time and energy then it is recommended to descend via Y Lliwedd. However if an easier route is preferred the return leg can be made via the Pig Track. The Y Lliwedd route is longer, involves a slippery descent off the summit of Snowdon followed by a stony ascent up to the twin summit peaks of Y Lliwedd; but compared with Crib Goch, it is easy and fairly safe (except in very high winds) while retaining at all times the exhilarating experience of being atop a fine ridge. The views of both the horseshoe and the wider area are marvellous.

The alternative, descending via the Pig Track, involves some re-tracing of the outwards route, but is significantly easier and less lengthy than the Y Lliwedd alternative. The views, on the descent of the track along a shelf or terrace on the slopes of Crib Goch and, on the last leg, looking down the Llanberis Pass, are fantastic.

Start along the wide, gravelly Miners' Track from the southern corner of the car park. The initial stages of the walk take you past plenty of outcrops of the Lower Rhyolitic Tuffs (LRT) which erupted during the main phase of volcanic activity in the area when the Snowdon 'caldera' collapsed. Most of what you see for quite a while are 'air-fall' tuffs, rock made from volcanic 'ash'. This produces rather unremarkable rocks, with few distinguishing features, except for some signs of later 'cleavage' (from forces exerted during the mountain-building phase). Initially there are wide views towards Carnedd y Cribau and some of the features seen on that walk can be viewed from a different perspective here (see if you can spot the diverted streams and the line of the watershed as mentioned in Walk 7; also some of the transverse fault lines are clearly visible).

After about ten minutes the tips of Y Lliwedd (left), then Snowdon and then Crib Goch (right) appear on the skyline. Almost immediately the track swings right (just after some work areas on the right) and the views open up dramatically towards the summit ridge ahead and, on the left, down into Cwm Dyli, the lowest of Snowdon's glacial cwms which overhangs Nant Gwynant. Looking down into the cwm you can see some lines of mounds – these are lateral moraines left by the declining glacier when it no longer filled the cwm, as would have been the case at the height of cwm glaciation.

After another few minutes the track again swings to the right and Llyn Teryn comes into view. It's debateable whether this small lake is in Cwm Dyli or Cwm Llydaw, or a mezzanine floor, cupped as it is in an upper corner of Cwm Dyli behind an 'andesitic' (i.e. intermediate between rhyolitic and basaltic) rock bar 75 metres above main cwm floor.

As you approach Llyn Teryn take a closer look at the rock bar, with its near-vertical crags overlooking the main floor of Cwm Dyli. You should be able to see clear signs of 'columnar jointing', some vertical, some slanting from lower right to upper left (see photos w1.1 and 5.5). This is produced by the way in which this intrusive andesite cooled after emplacement and is not uncommon in volcanic rocks.

Photo w1.1 | Columnar jointing, intrusive andesite outcrop, near Llyn Teryn.

The sharp, steep dolerite crags mark the back wall of Cwm Dyli and the threshold of Cwm Llydaw. The same intrusion extends beyond the rock bar and runs up as part of the blunt nose to the ridge line to the left of Y Lliwedd (see photo 5.5). More of the intrusion, and some more columnar jointing, can be seen way up in the outcrops to the right, way above the track.

Another five minutes or so along the track and the views start to extend all the way into Cwm Llydaw, with a new vista opening out magnificently. You are surrounded by crags that rear upwards all around. Perhaps Crib Goch is the most impressive prominence, its sharp eastern ridge giving a good flavour of this glacial arête (see photo w1.9). Note too the great thick veins of quartz that can be seen in the cliffs on either side intruded between the layers of rock visible on Crib Goch and on the Y Lliwedd Ridge. Also you can see some of the large moraines in the cwm. This is a spot at which you really need to stop and sit down for a few minutes to appreciate the great variety of glacial features.

The track crosses the lake on a causeway, built for copper mining operations, then swings left towards a large moraine on the right (see photo w1.3 taken from just before crossing the

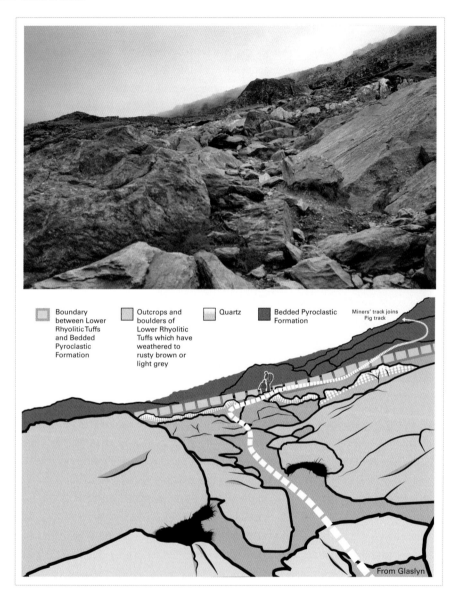

Legend:
- Boundary between Lower Rhyolitic Tuffs and Bedded Pyroclastic Formation
- Outcrops and boulders of Lower Rhyolitic Tuffs which have weathered to rusty brown or light grey
- Quartz
- Bedded Pyroclastic Formation

Miners' track joins Pig track

From Glaslyn

Photo w1.2 + diagram w1.1 | Miners' Track – boundary between Lower Rhyolitic Tuffs (lighter-coloured rocks in foreground) and Bedded Pyroclastic Formation (darker rocks in upper half of photo behind red-jacketed walker) – see photo 4.10 for a closer view of this rock. The line of white quartz rocks mark the boundary. This scene is just below where the Miners' Track joins the Pig Track.

Photo w1.3 | Llyn Llydaw and glacial moraine (centre); Y Lliwedd (left); Snowdon summit (right).

causeway). Again, the rock outcrops just above you are all LRT. A while later you pass ruins from the mining and then the track leaves the lake to rise gradually towards Glaslyn, and the start of the ascent towards the summit.

Glaslyn arrives suddenly; the first glimpse right into the cwm comes when the stream suddenly becomes a flow out of the lake. Up until then the rock bar, still LRT, that holds in the lake prevents any views into the cwm. Follow the track round to the start of the serious ascent marked by a standing stone and a recently improved track (starting at 6170 5471). There follows a stiff, twisting climb up through outcrops of the LRT, until after 10-15 minutes or so (and shortly before meeting the Pig Track) you pass into the Bedded Pyroclastic Formation (BPF) (see photo w1.2 and diagram w1.1). If you keep a look out up and ahead, you should see the change coming as you ascend, the outcrops becoming noticeably darker in colour than the light-to-reddish-brown outcrops of the LRT. A thick vein of quartz that you follow for a couple of metres also helps mark the boundary.

All the outcrops you pass from here until shortly below the summit are part of the BPF. Carry on until you meet the Pig Track (at a standing stone) and turn left. You can clearly see bedding in these darker rocks (a mixture of basaltic lavas, tuffs and sedimentary rocks). Also, you can see a considerable variety of breccias in the slabs used to make up the track – however many if not most of these will have been brought in by helicopter and cannot be used as a guide to the bedrock around here.

Snowdon

Keep a look out for Glaslyn Bach on the left, the highest of the glacial cwms in the Snowdon Horseshoe and site of copper mining. If you go off to have a look at this tiny cwm, take very great care getting there and back onto the Pig Track, as there are some unguarded holes in the ground with big drops from the mining of narrow seams of minerals.

Once you arrive at the 'zigzag' section of the Pig Track you are not far from reaching Bwlch Glas (which is at 998 metres above sea level). At the bwlch (the junction is marked by a standing stone) you are greeted by a sudden outward expansion of views, which appear all the more impressive after having been so long enclosed within the walls of the great staircase of cwms. Here too, in summer, you may be greeted by the puffing (or if diesel, whining) train engine from the Snowdon Mountain Railway whose railroad now accompanies the walkers' track for the final 85 metres of ascent.

Shortly before the summit (though you may not notice it if distracted by the pull of the objective) the track passes a flat, grassy area which marks the change from the BPF to a few outcrops of the last of the Snowdon volcanic group rocks, the Upper Rhyolitic Tuffs (URT). These tuffs are mixed with sedimentary rocks which can contain fossils of shelled marine animals, though you will need luck and/or close attention to spot them.

Photo w1.4 | View north-west from summit of Snowdon towards Moel Cynghorion and Moel Eilio, both peaking through a cloud inversion.

Photo w1.5 | A 'Brockenspectre' or 'Glory' from the summit of Snowdon reflected onto the flanks of Crib y Ddysgyl.

From the summit the views on a good day are truly excellent and at times it is possible to see as far as the Wicklow Mountains to the south of Dublin, to the Isle of Man and to the southern Scottish Isles – but such days are regrettably very, very few and far between. Even if the summit is clear of cloud, visibility is usually less extensive, but you can still fairly often see as far as Cader Idris and the Berwyns – both distant outcrops of rocks from the same Ordovician volcanic cycles that produced the rocks of central Snowdonia. Even if the air is very hazy you should be able to see the glacial architecture of Snowdon and its neighbouring mountain ranges.

Even if there is cloud about, don't be put off. Some of the most magnificent views come when the summit is above clouds which coat the lower parts of the mountain or when the cloud is lifting.

The summit of Snowdon can be an extremely crowded place on busy days and even in bad weather you'll probably meet several other people seeking shelter from the wind and rain while eating lunch.

The return route to Pen y Pass via Y Lliwedd at first involves a short detour. Initially head south-west on the track towards Snowdon's south ridge, rather than heading directly towards Y Lliwedd from the summit (though an inviting looking route from the summit, it soon leads

Snowdon

Photo w1.6 | Marker stone for descent to Y Lliwedd, shrouded in cloud.

to very steep ground). After about five minutes of descent (past outcrops of the BPF) you come to a short level stretch and a standing stone on the left marking the start of the track to Bwlch y Saethau (see photo w1.6). The track provides a slithery diagonal descent across Snowdon's south-eastern face, providing dramatic views into Cwm Llan, and shortly brings you out onto Bwlch y Saethau where you cross back into the LRT. From here on there are great views down into the Snowdon Horseshoe and to the other mountain ranges to the south.

The main track is on the right of the ridge but, for a lot more effort in return for much better views, you can follow the ridgeline itself up, over and down different outcrops.

In either case, when you get to the start of the climb up Y Lliwedd, choose one of the many tracks which twist and turn upwards to the twin peaks which make for superlative viewpoints and, wind permitting, excellent spots for a break and a drink. You cross out of the LRT and back into the BPF shortly after starting to descend towards and past Lliwedd Bach (again there's a choice of the main or a higher track).

Photo w1.7 | View from east summit of Y Lliwedd towards summit of Snowdon.

Photo w1.8 | View down to Llyn Llydaw from near summit of Y Lliwedd.

The track starts to descend from the ridge line at a cairn at about 6305 5350 on a nose or bluff of rock (marked by a cairn). The most difficult section comes shortly after the start of the descent where a steep rock outcrop has to be scrambled down for 5 metres or so.

The descent of this bluff of rock, sticking out from the cliffs on either side, follows close to the junction between the BPF on the right and the LRT to the left, until near the base, when the track moves back into the BPF – see photo w1.8, which was taken from just below the summit of Y Lliwedd. Near the base of the nose, you may spot some intensely marked darkish rocks on the left of the track (and elsewhere). These are 'hyaloclastites', a rock formed by the explosive eruption of basaltic lava undersea level.

The track takes you through moraines to Llyn Llydaw where it rejoins the Miners' Track to return to Pen y Pass to end an outing on Wales's most magnificent mountain.

Photo w1.9 |
Moraine and
Llyn Llydaw
(foreground);
Snowdon (upper
left centre); Crib
Goch (upper right).

Descent via the Pig Track

If you prefer an easier descent this provides a suitable option while still offering fantastic views. From the summit of Snowdon, the return journey initially uses the same route as you used to get here, so return beside the railway track to Bwlch Glas and the standing stone at the top of the Pig Track. Then follow the Pig Track all the way back to Pen y Pass.

The views are excellent. First you get views down into the staircase of cwms as you descend towards the point where the Miners' Track joined the Pig Track. When you reach this point, carry on along the Pig Track round a bowl high above Glaslyn, passing as you go from the BPF to LRT tuffs.

Note the Y Gribau ridge rising to Bwlch y Saethau on the other side of Glaslyn. The ridge is the uppermost part of the rock bar impounding Glaslyn. The rock bar rises on this side of the lake to form the prominence (made of intrusive rhyolite) to which you head as you go round the bowl.

At the end of the bowl a small outcrop needs to be scrambled over where the track bears sharp left. Do remember to stop here and turn round for a classic view of Snowdon's summit and the glacial cwm at its foot. The view of the rock wall between Glaslyn and the summit is sensational, a testimony to the power of a cwm glacier.

The track then carries on along a shelf on the flank of Crib Goch. This marks the boundary between rock types. The shelf is made of the BPF, while the steeper slopes below are formed from LRT tuffs and the steep slope above is intrusive rhyolite. Views to the lower parts of the horseshoe and to Y Lliwedd are superb. Crib Goch, a mass of intrusive rhyolite, rises, bulky and domineering, above you on the left.

Eventually you reach Bwlch y Moch (the pass of the pigs or the swine) and the track leaves the horseshoe for an amazing traverse along the northern side of the last part of the horseshoe, on its outer flank. The views of the great glacial trench of the Llanberis Pass are stunning. You also pass a variety of outcrops on your right, first the BPF, then great buttresses of intrusive rhyolite, and finally the last buttress, shortly before turning the corner to Pen y Pass, air-fall tuffs of the LRT (the same as seen as the start of the walk on the Miners' Track).

Photo w2.1 | Tryfan, Glyder Fach and Glyder Fawr viewed from Y Garn.

Y Glyderau

The Glyderau ridge runs from near Bethesda in the north to Capel Curig in the east, with a sharp right-angle bend in the ridge at the western end of Llyn Ogwen. The whole range is worth visiting, but necessarily the primary attention focuses on three spectacularly interesting mountains, Glyder Fawr, Glyder Fach and Tryfan. Their scenic and geological qualities make them well worth our close attention.

These three mountains cluster at the point where the ridge does its turn from running north-south to west-east and in the angle between them they have managed to enclose a complex set of glacial cwms at different heights. The glaciers also removed masses of rock from here, exposing a classic 'syncline' in the Snowdon Volcanic Group rocks and as well as depositing an array of moraines. The combination of features makes this area one of the most impressive mountain sights in Britain and it should not be missed by visitors if at all possible.

The classic walk on the Glyderau encompasses Tryfan, Glyder Fach and Glyder Fawr, with a descent of the marvellous Twll Du (Black Chasm, but known as the Devil's Kitchen). To do them all in one go, however, makes for a pretty long walk, leaving little if any time to dawdle and soak up the atmosphere or study the landscape.

The most popular route includes the challenging scrambles on Tryfan's North Ridge and Bristly Ridge on Glyder Fach. There are walking alternatives (such as via Llyn Bochlwyd and the Miners' Track) but whatever route is chosen, this is a pretty demanding walk.

To provide routes of manageable length, I have divided the walks on the three mountains into three separate routes. Two walks start and end at or near Idwal Cottage, while the third commences from either Pen y Pass or Pen y Gwryd.

The Glyder Fawr walk is a pared down version of the classic round, starting from Idwal Cottage. It involves a part-scramble up Gribin to the summit and the not-to-be-missed descent via Twll Du.

For Tryfan I outline two possible routes, the long but reasonably safe scramble up the north ridge, or the semi-scramble via the amazing 'Heather Terrace' (a fascinating geological feature in itself) and down through Cwm Tryfan.

For Glyder Fach, I recommend a different approach, one that will reveal the less familiar flank of both Glyder Fach and Glyder Fawr, as well as passing a variety of geological features and great views. This walk could easily be altered, if desired, to include the summit of Glyder Fawr without adding very significantly to its overall length.

I've also added two more walks on the northern ridge of the Glyderau to show some other facets of this marvellous ridge. Walk 6 guides you over Elidir Fawr and other peaks at the northern tip of the ridge, and walk 8 which takes you past a series of glacial cwms on the north-eastern section of the ridge.

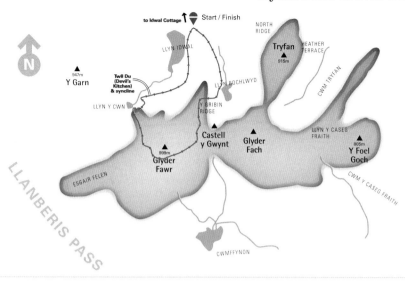

Walk #2
Glyder Fawr & Twll Du

START	▶	NEAR OGWEN COTTAGE, BUS STOP AND CAR PARKS (6505 6036)
FINISH	●	CIRCULAR ROUTE
TIME	◔	5 HOURS PLUS
GRADE	⊕	NAVIGATION ● ● ●
	◬	TERRAIN ● ● ● ● ●
	◈	SEVERITY ● ● ● ● ●

Glyder Fawr, like its only very slightly lower counterpart Glyder Fach, is an amazing mountain. Its summit area is a rocky excess, with numerous 'tors' – small rock outcrops sticking up above the main level. Especially in misty weather these tors make for an otherworldly atmosphere, though even in clear weather this is a mountain summit that impresses itself deeply on the walker who makes it all the way up.

The route is quite tough and requires a reasonable head for heights, but should be within the capabilities of any reasonably fit hillwalker who enjoys a challenge. The variety of views encompassed in such a comparatively short walk is outstanding by any measure. The route is possible in the mist but would then require extremely good and careful navigation – the main difficulty being ensuring you get onto the right track for descent from the summit and then avoiding losing it before the start of the scree slope.

Start from the National Park Authority centre, nestled between Ogwen Cottage and Idwal Cottage, following the main track, roughly south-east, as it crosses a stream and climbs through rock outcrops. Where the main track swings away right (south-west), at about 6515 6015, leave the main track and carry on south-east on a muddy track, heading towards Nant Bochlwyd. It eventually becomes a stone track which then climbs up beside the stream as it tumbles down from the 'hanging valley' above, enclosing Llyn Bochlwyd.

The climb takes you up past outcrops and boulders of both sedimentary rocks and Capel Curig Volcanic rocks (the CCV was produced by the main eruptions of the LLewelyn Volcanic Group – see Walk 5 in the Carneddau). As you climb and watch the multitude of small waterfalls, you can imagine the glacial 'icefall' that would have existed here as the glacier that poured out of Cwm Bochlwyd towards the end of the ice age.

This is an utterly delightful section of the route, but is soon over and a new scene is unfolded as you enter Cwm Bochlwyd. Tryfan to the left, the main face of Glyder Fach straight ahead beyond Llyn Bochlwyd, and the Gribin Ridge to the right.

A path heads off to the right as you reach the cwm, but for the best route, stick with the stream all the way up to the lake, then bear right towards the bottom of Gribin Ridge. Gribin is an arête (as is Tryfan) i.e. a sharp ridge left between two glacial cwms, created as their glaciers dug back into their sidewalls reducing them to a common sharp ridge.

Head to the bottom of Gribin and pick up the track to ascend the blunt ridge. The first rocks you encounter, on your left, are CCV tuffs. Then after a short while you come across cleaved sedimentary rocks on your right; you may well be able to see fossils in some of these sedimentary rocks between here and the point where the ridge widens out. Higher up, you can see breccias of the CCV, again on the right. Where the ridge widens out into a wide gently sloping plateau, the Pitts Head Tuffs (PHT) of 'False Gribin' come in from the left and form the narrow ridge that rears up to the summit plateau. See w2.2 and diagram w2.1.

Viewed from the Gribin Ridge

Diagram w2.1 + Photo w2.2 | Tryfan and Llyn Bochlwyd from Y Gribin Ridge.

The cool-headed may want to stick to the crest of the ridge from here for fantastic views into Cwm Bochlwyd on the left and Cwm Cneifion on the right. Others may prefer the less heady track that stays, fairly safely, just below the crest of the ridge on the right hand side. It's a stiff climb with sections of steep scrambling, but the rocks are secure in the dry and offer plentiful foot and hand holds. The important thing is to avoid straying too far below the crest – make sure that you keep heading up, to stay as close as you can to the skyline.

Glyder Fawr & Twll Du

The views, you will no doubt have noticed, just keep on getting better and better on this fantastic climb through a stunning glacial landscape with cwms and their sharp separating arêtes all around.

Then suddenly the slope eases off and you arrive on the eastern end of Glyder Fawr's summit plateau, just above Bwlch Ddwy Glyder. Castell y Gwynt, to the left just beyond the bwlch, demands attention, its well-jointed rhyolitic rocks running straight down the main face of Glyder Fach and out of view. From this viewpoint the lower part of Castell y Gwynt is a truly untidy pile of rocks. The view west towards Snowdon is also magnificent (see photo w2.3).

Photo w2.3 | View west to Snowdon (right) and Y Lliwedd (centre).

However, we turn right, and head up towards the summit of Glyder Fawr, first on stone-strewn grass, but increasingly on a carpet of stones-cum-boulders. Then there appear some of the many summit tors, the product of freeze-thaw action of water on joints in the rocks. Some of the tors are quite large, others middling in size, while many have been reduced to little more than stumps (see photo 7.9).

The summit plateau encompasses several different types of rock – roughly from south to north, Pitts Head Tuff, sedimentary rocks, basalt lava, maybe (depending on your exact line)

Photo w2.4 | 'Five finger' tor.

some dolerite, then, up to the summit, lots of intrusive rhyolite, and outcrops of the Lower Rhyolitic Tuffs (LRT) at the summit tors and beyond. The effect of freeze-thaw action varies with the type of rock and its jointing, producing different shapes in the tors and you can use these differences to identify different types of rock.

In good weather it pays to spend some time walking round the edge of the summit plateau, especially on the side overlooking Nant Ffrancon. Otherwise, the cairned track guides you to the two summit tors.

Finding the route down may be difficult in the mist and can even be confusing in clear weather. The track (shown as a dashed black line on the OS map) starts from between the two summit tors and heads round the south-west side of the western summit tor, passes between that tor and another smaller one and then drops down, now heading north-west.

Nature has provided a useful way-marker some 25 metres off to the left of the track, about 150 metres after leaving the summit – a tor that bears a passing resemblance to five fingers sticking upwards. It is visible in all but the thickest of mists. (See photo w2.4).

The track then swings right, away from the five-fingered tor, down across more loose rocks, eventually reaching a flat, stony grass area, near a patch of quartz pebbles. It is important here to swing further to the right to pick up the cairned track down.

After five minutes or so, the stony track starts to steepen, suddenly dipping down dramatically, opening up views to the bwlch below. The next five minutes of descent, down a steep scree gully, are pure slithery hell, but the worst is soon over as the slope becomes progressively less steep. There are several routes down the last section of the slope, all bringing you out at the blwch near Llyn y Cwn (the lake of the dogs).

This bwlch is one of the 'secondary glacial breaching points', created when the outlet glacier of the ice cap forced its way over the mountain ridge from the Llanberis Pass into Cwm Idwal and Nant Ffrancon, exploiting the structural weakness running through here from right (north-east) to left (south-west), the site of one of the great faultlines and also where the rocks were folded by mountain-building forces to create a great syncline (which we will soon start to descend) also running across the bwlch between Glyder Fawr behind us and Y Garn in front.

Photo w2.5 (left) | 'Pillow lava' at the head of Twll Du (Devil's Kitchen) – formed by basaltic lava eruption below sea-level.

Photo w2.6 (above) | Ripple marks.

Here a diversion is recommended to the outlet stream of the lake and then down to the top of Twll Du. Here you not only get great views, but also the chance to see basaltic 'pillow lavas', created as the lava is erupted undersea, cooling into the rounded 'pillow-shaped' blobs you can here see solidified into rock (see photo w2.5). Do not attempt to descend here as the gully soon becomes a greasy vertical cliff!

Return to the bottom of the track down from Glyder Fawr, and at about 6382 5850 meet and follow the track gently downwards to the top of the Twll Du path. Descend through increasingly impressive outcrops of the Bedded Pyroclast Formation (BPF) – mainly basaltic

Photo w2.7 | View down from near Twll Du to Llyn Idwal, with moraines on either side of the lake.

lavas, tuffs and sedimentary rocks, clearly bedded – on the left. Watch out for ripple marks in outcrops of the top of the LRT on the right (see photo w2.6). These are 're-worked' (eroded from similar tuffs nearby and laid down as sedimentary rocks here); lower down there is a variety of tuffs and breccias within the LRT.

The path suddenly starts to swing left and the views open out over Cwm Idwal. This moment is one of the highlights of walking in Snowdonia. Amazingly, the views continue to improve – and at the same time the track gets ever steeper, but it has been upgraded and makes excellent use of rocks as steps. Big awkward steps to be sure, but well worth the effort.

As you descend here you are walking on one of the exposed rock boundaries of the great Idwal syncline (which carries on via Snowdon to Moel Hebog), one of the major geological structures of central Snowdonia. The arm or ledge of the syncline has been etched into the boundary between the BPF above you and the LRT below.

Take your time here. First, so that you do not fall on the steep steps. Second, to enjoy the views of the Idwal Slabs to the right (famous climbing cliffs in 'air-fall tuffs' of the LRT), Llyn Idwal below and its complex of moraines, the glacial breaching face of Pen yr Ole Wen straight ahead, Nant Ffrancon and Y Garn to the left. Third, to enjoy time to look at the variety of rocks all around, both in the crags and in the 'rockfall' all around you. These blocks fell down after the glacier had melted, leaving oversteepened and unstable crags (a fate awaiting many present day glacial valleys throughout the world as a result of human-induced climate change).

When you reach the centre of the syncline, the views open out once again and you stand above a mad chaos of fallen blocks of rock (see photo w2.7). Descend, looking out for a minor track on the left which provides an optional diversion to the base of the Twll Du, truly a black chasm. Return to the main track and continue down to the point where the track splits into two. The route to the right looks more direct. But it involves a potentially difficult stream crossing which necessitates some 'rock-hopping' and where a slip could well be serious.

The left-hand track involves one or two initial small scrambles, but overall is easier and is not actually any longer. It also takes you right through the impressive moraines on Llyn Idwal's western side. If you turn round frequently, from the time you meet the moraines until you cross the footbridge further on, you have the very best views there are of the great syncline (see photo 5.3) and also the 'hanging valley' of Cwm Cneifion to its left. So, this side gets my recommendation as a fitting way to finish to one of Snowdonia's very best landscape walks.

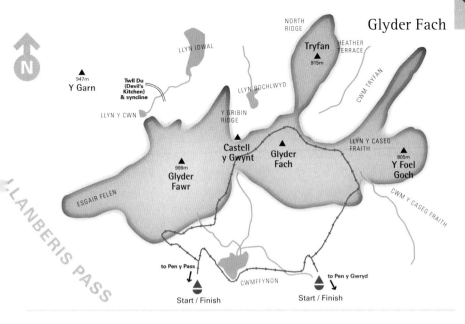

Walk #3 Glyder Fach

START	▶	PEN Y PASS – (6470 5566) OR PEN Y GWRYD (6610 5595)
FINISH	●	CIRCULAR ROUTE
TIME	◔	5 HOURS PLUS
GRADE	⊙	NAVIGATION ● ● ● ● ●
	☁	TERRAIN ● ● ● ● ●
	✦	SEVERITY ● ● ● ● ●

Glyder Fach is a surreal mountain. Its rocky summit is a mass of great blocks of stone lying at all angles. It is like some half-finished quarry, where the rock has been broken up but not carted away. It is one of those few mountains that even looks interesting in the mist and certainly frosty weather can make it look even more otherworldly.

The overall walk, unhurried, takes a good five or six hours, some of it on rough and remote terrain, and it can be navigationally challenging in getting the right route on the descent from Bwlch Ddwy Glyder. It is thus not recommended in misty conditions.

Glyder Fach

The walk starts and ends at either Pen y Pass (for bus users and early bird car drivers) or Pen y Gwryd (for those who get to Pen y Pass after the car park is full). From Pen y Pass: start at the garden at the northern end of the YHA hostel, and follow the track up the hillside to the crest of the low ridge, ascending through 'air-fall' tuffs, outcrops of the Lower Rhyolitic Tuffs (LRT). On reaching the crest of the ridge, pick a path to the left of Llyn Cwmffynnon and aim for 'spot height' 379 to the north of the lake. Then contour across, following the bottom of the steep slope, aiming for a stile in the stone wall at about 6613 5648. Cross the wall and immediately turn left on the Miners' Track. The going is rough and often boggy but is soon over.

From Pen y Gwryd: cross the stile at 6610 5595 and follow the initially quite boggy track, heading just east of north (marked on OS map). Cross the footbridge and follow the track, with stone wall on the left, passing a stile at 6610 5648 where the route from Pen y Pass joins.

Both routes: Continue to head just east of north on the track, passing through dolerite outcrops and boulders; at about 66190 56675, cross the stone wall on a stile just after the wall turns sharply right.

Up as far as the stone wall the track has crossed boggy ground, underlain by sedimentary rocks and the dolerite intrusion. Now there are plenty of boulders and erratics, but few outcrops; however the geology maps tell us that tuffs of the Capel Curig Volcanics form the underlying rocks from about the point where the last stile was crossed. The geological and botanical boundaries both lie where the slope becomes steeper and the vegetation becomes dominated by heather rather than grass. The CCV rocks were erupted by the last and biggest eruptions of the Llewelyn Volcanic Group (see Walk 5 in the Carneddau for more information about this eruptive cycle).

Photo w3.1

Large block of breccia on Miners' Track (boulder measures about 2m across).

Continue on up the track, passing more good examples of breccia on the way (e.g. 6652 5712). At about 6662 5725 the rocks change from tuffs to breccias, still part of the CCVs. There is a massive block of breccia next to the track at 6666 5731 (see photo w3.1).

Looking upwards from here, you can see that there are clear outcrops on the skyline. You meet these outcrops shortly after the track crosses the stream (at about 6672 5751). These rocks are intrusive rhyolite and form a craggy edge to the ridge. There is some 'columnar jointing' to be seen from outcrops on the right shortly after the waterfall marked on the OS maps. Carry on up towards the crags.

I recommend a short diversion soon after the track reaches the rhyolite crags. When the angle of the slope eases, turn right and head east for about 200 metres (to about 6698 5784) so that you are overlooking the basin called Cwm y Caseg Fraith.

It's worth spending a little time mulling over the scenery here and trying to interpret the landscape. What initially looks like little more than a desolate, wet depression, with little to attract the walker's interest, is actually full of information about the way in which geology and scenery interact.

Look closely at the cwm below you. It has a higher and a lower bowl, with various piles of rocks and outcrops within the bowls. These outcrops separate the subsidiary boggy basins. Looking at the summit beyond the cwm (Y Foel Goch) you can see that there are several terraces on the right-hand side of the hill as it descends to just beyond Cwm y Caseg Fraith. The highest is a clear, wide terrace and lower down there are two or three less conspicuous ones (depending on where you are the lowest terrace may not be visible). (See photo w3.2 and diagram w3.1).

Let's start with these terraces. The upper, wide, terrace marks the boundary between the intrusive rhyolite which forms the summit of Y Foel Goch (the same rhyolite as you climbed through and are now surrounded by) and the CCV forming the slope below the terrace. The lower terraces are less immediately obvious as they are little more than hiccups in the steady slope downwards but can be distinguished on closer inspection. These each represent a dolerite intrusion.

The terraces thus result from the existence of junctions between rock types and from the interplay of comparative resistance of different rock types to erosion by ice and water and to chemical weathering.

Turning to the cwm itself, at first glance the mounds of loose rocks, separating the boggy basins, look rather like moraines. Closer examination shows that the mounds of loose rocks actually surround solid outcrops. The loose rocks are also very similar to all the other loose rocks on the hillsides above and beyond the cwm and all around you. They

Glyder Fach

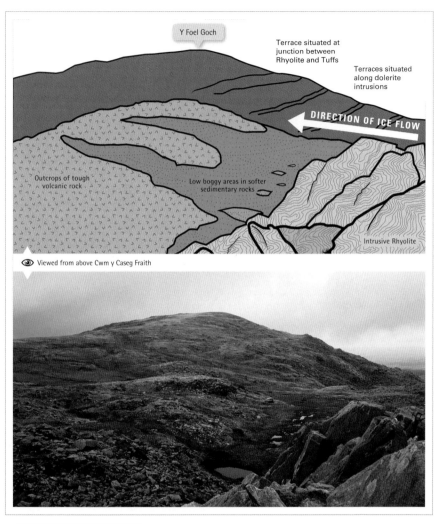

Diagram w3.1 + Photo w3.2 | Cwm y Caseg Fraith.

obviously aren't all moraines. The loose rocks are in fact the product of freeze-thaw action, which prizes them out of the exposed outcrops of bedrock. The geology map tells us that these outcrops are tongues of tougher volcanic rocks and the basins are underlain by softer sedimentary rocks.

So what has happened here? During the ice age the outlet glacier, from the Migneint ice sheet, breached the Glyderau ridge here (and at other points too). The ice went from south to north, coming up the slope you have climbed, continuing over Bwlch y Caseg Fraith and down into Cwm Tryfan, and also across Bwlch Tryfan and down via Cwm Bochlwyd.

A fault, trending east to west, crosses the slope below Cwm y Caseg Fraith and subsequent earth movements have brought more of the sedimentary rocks to the surface around this and nearby parallel faults. The cwm has developed on these weaknesses under pressure from the mass of ice exploiting the relative resistance of the sedimentary rocks on the one hand and the intrusive rhyolite and CCV rocks on the other.

I have taken this example, not to illustrate any particular feature, but to show how you can start to read the landscape in surprisingly considerable detail, even in apparently uninteresting areas.

Obviously it helps if you have a geology map, but even without a map it should be possible to work out that a terrace between outcrops is probably a geological boundary or weakness of some sort. Such terraces often make useful walking routes – you'll see one of the most famous when you get onto the ridge in a few minutes, the Heather Terrace on Tryfan formed by an outcrop of weak sedimentary rock with rhyolite above and CCV below. Also the recommended descent on this walk, from Bwlch Ddwy Glyder, makes use of a geologically-determined terrace.

Let's leave this desolate spot, crossing boggy grass, heading towards Llyn y Caseg Fraith (see photo w3.3) on the northern side of the ridge, where we can begin the ascent up to Glyder Fach. The views open up dramatically, towards Tryfan (with its highly conspicuous Heather Terrace rising from lower right to upper left across its steep flank) and the Carneddau.

Photo w3.3 | Tryfan from Bwlch y Caseg Fraith.

Glyder Fach

Photo w3.4 | The summit of Glyder Fach – a pile of freeze-thaw rock tors and boulder-fields.

The sedimentary rocks underfoot (hidden by vegetation) soon give way to rhyolite, at the first outcrops to be encountered, at about 66439 58227. Continue up on the cairned track, through more rhyolite outcrops, until about 6600 5837 where the rock changes to large slabs of breccia, part of the CCV. The slope also gets markedly steeper and it is necessary now and again to use the hands to scramble up the slabs. The track is cairned, but twists and turns rapidly, so is easily lost. On reaching the summit plateau, bear left (just south of west) along the northern edge of the summit, enjoying the incomparably grand views of Tryfan, the Carneddau and the northern Glyderau.

Pass the much-photographed 'cantilever rock' and the summit tor, then drop down heading towards Castell y Gwynt (Castle of the Wind) – see photos w3.5 and 7.8. These crazy rock formations are the result of freeze-thaw action during and after the ice age. It is thought that the summits stood above the ice and were exposed after the ice age to many thousands of years of water freezing in joints in the rocks, freezing, expanding, thawing and so on again and again, cracking open the rocks and leaving them in the mad patterns we see today.

A good scramble can be had by crossing Castell y Gwynt directly, or for an easier descent, follow the track (a cairn marks its start) to the left (south-west) down to Bwlch Ddwy Glyder.

Photo w3.5 (top) | The Cantilever Rock.   Photo w3.6 (bottom) | Castell y Gwynt.

The walk is easily extended from here to Glyder Fawr, then descending on the track marked on the OS map on Glyder Fawr's south-west ridge – this highly twisty route is way-marked by faint red paint marks on rocks (though these only start some way down and it can be hard to find the start of the 'red route' track in the mist).

The recommended route omits the summit of Glyder Fawr and instead drops down onto the terrace below the steep rocky slopes of Waun Gron (see photo w3.6) and joins the 'red route' later on.

Glyder Fach

Photo w3.7 | Descent route via a terrace on flank of Glyder Fawr (Pitts Head Tuff above right; sedimentary rocks on the terrace; and Capel Curig Volcanics on the steep slope, below left). The route descends to Llyn Cwmffynnon, lower left. Snowdon in background.

In the mist it could be very difficult to find both the start of the recommended route and more especially the part beyond the terrace until it joins the 'red route'. However, in good weather the route into the terrace from just beyond Bwlch Ddwy Glyder is pretty obvious. As you drop down to the Bwlch, don't take what appears to be a path at the lowest point you reach, but continue along the main track for another 25 metres as it re-ascends slightly and swings to the right, until another track branches off left, at 6528 5811. This track initially follows a bearing of 235°, but soon swings left to a bearing of about 225° (south-west).

As you drop down, the terrace becomes quite wide and provides a fresh view of southern slopes of Glyder Fach. Above you, forming the steep slope, are the tough Pitts Head Tuffs, the first eruption in the main Snowdon Volcanic Group. The terrace is sedimentary rock (with some fascinating rock shapes to be seen) and the steep slope below the terrace, and forming the rim of outcrops along its edge, are CCV rocks. If you have the energy and inclination it's worth leaving the track and picking a route along the rim of CCV outcrops. If you do this you may well come across some rocks with 'siliceous nodules', varying from the size of marbles down to that of peas, with later cleavage lines cutting across the nodules.

Carry on down into a second terrace, or really more of a bowl or steeply sloping basin, following an ever fainter track. This area is underlain by sedimentary rocks. Cross the streams debouching to the left. The narrow track has all but disappeared by here and it is necessary to starting re-gaining some height to cross the steep rock outcrops ahead marking the end of the basin. You need only gain enough height (no more than about 25 metres over a distance of 200 metres) to get safely past the outcrops.

This section may be extremely difficult in the mist (I haven't had the occasion to try it under such conditions and have no desire to do so) as it would be hard to discern a route. Even in clear weather you lose sight of the ridge which you will later follow downwards. However, carry on, picking a line above the outcrops. If you take a look at the outcrops themselves as you pass over them you may recognise them as the Pitts Head Tuff with some siliceous nodules and some welded tuffs.

Once past the outcrops carry on at the same height, until at about 6394 5704 you should suddenly meet an obvious track cutting across your direction of travel (in a boggy slight depression); this is the 'red route' (so-called because its route is marked by fading red blobs of paint on boulders alongside it). Turn left and join the red route track through a gap in the rocks.

If time and energy permits, another small diversion is well worth the effort. Immediately after passing through the gap in the rocks you enter another grassy area between outcrops. The 'red route' carries straight on between a narrow gap, but instead turn right and walk along the grassy area with outcrops of the LRT on either side, until suddenly, and very emphatically, you find yourself overlooking the Llanberis Pass and staring straight at the slopes below Crib Goch. The view here of Crib Goch and Cwm Beudy Mawr is almost overwhelming in intensity as you stare straight into the upper reaches of the cwm, surely one of the most dramatic views in Snowdonia (see photo 6.17).

To continue, return to the 'red route' track and follow it through the gap in the rocks (where the LRT outcrops are very well displayed) and then steeply downhill. The route twists and turns between outcrops and is easy to lose. There are several places where the track diverges and really any one route is as good as any other, though, if you can find it, the marked route is probably the easiest line, minimising the need for scrambling.

After the initial steep descent you come to a flatter area (with some pretty wet patches) and, on your left, you should pass an expanse of an exposed bedding plane in sedimentary rocks with quite clear glacial scratch marks or 'striae' (see photo w3.8); then shortly further

Photo w3.8 | Glacial scratches ('striae') in exposed sandstone bedding plane.

on you once again meet the Pitts Head Tuff, with plenty of siliceous nodules to be seen. Staying with the 'red route', you pass onto sedimentary rock and then cross some basalt lava outcrops as you descend over one or two more steep sections. At the bottom the track swings left (south-east) to head back across a boggy low area towards the LRT outcrops above Pen y Pass and the track back to there.

To return to Pen y Gwryd, before reaching the low boggy ground, aim well to the left of the LRT ridge, passing to the right of the lake and just below some outcrops about 25 metres higher than the lake. Then contour to beyond the lake (stepping over a low wire fence as necessary). Carry on to the crags and then bear north (see if you can spot the LRT rocks here and the junction with dolerite). Gain about 25 metres of height (to about 6525 5600, shortly after the last of the dolerite crags) before descending (across more boggy ground) directly to the starting stile (by aiming just to the left of the hotel grounds).

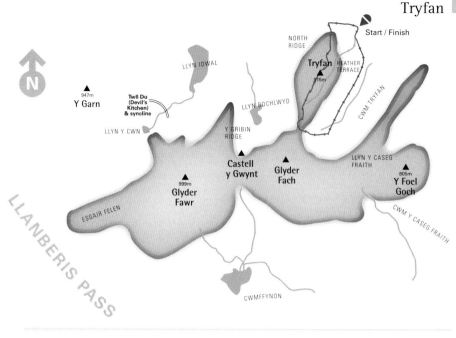

Walk #4 Tryfan

Tryfan is a very special mountain. Its most outstanding characteristic is simply that – it stands out. Its striking shape demands the attention from wherever it can be seen. Whether from a distance or from close up, it is an impressive mass of rocky mountain. Both from its flanks and from its summit area, it is a consistently stunning viewing point. Clearly Tryfan is a geological accident. We owe the existence of this exquisite peak to the specific interplay on this mountain of volcanic eruption, sedimentation, folding, uplift and extensive glacial erosion.

Tryfan's bony ridge is made up of rhyolitic tuffs and intrusive rhyolite and is not far from the centre of volcanic fissure-vents of the last and most powerful eruptive phase of the Llewelyn Volcanic Group (the phase which created the Capel Curig Volcanic (CCV) formation of rocks – see Walk 5). Its summit crest, running roughly north-east to south-west, runs parallel to the axis of an anticline in Cwm Tryfan, where mountain-building forces folded the rocks. Tryfan's narrow summit ridge is also an arête, a narrow ridge of rock left as glaciers on either side have cut back into the rock, and the bwlch or col between it and Glyder Fach is a secondary glacial breaching point where ice flowed down into Nant Ffrancon.

In many ways Tryfan exemplifies the best of Snowdonia's landscape – an intensely impressive rocky mountain with superb views. Yet despite its forbidding visage, Tryfan is within the reach of the fit walker – albeit any climb up to its summit, or down from it, demands some use of the hands as well as the feet.

The scramble up Tryfan's north ridge is one of Snowdonia's premiere routes for fit, confident hillwalkers. It is pretty safe as scrambles go, with a series minor scrambles up short crags, with good wide ledges between each short section – though it gets a bit tougher towards the top. All the same, don't dismiss the dangers too lightly – there's always the risk of slipping and falling a few metres, enough to break a leg or bash the head rather badly; all in a place where evacuation could be difficult.

So, as an alternative route I've added the option of leaving out the scramble and using the Heather Terrace which rises diagonally up and across the south-western face. This too is a super walk and does in any case deserve to be done in its own right (for example if the summit is in the clouds). It's a walk rather than a scramble, but only just. It is quite tough, possibly hard to find in the early stages, rising at a steep angle up and over roughly tumbled boulders, and finally needing a short, steep scrabble up some scree to arrive at the bwlch or col between Tryfan's main summit and its 'South Peak'.

It's a tough choice, but for the return leg I've described the route through Cwm Tryfan. Cwm Bochlwyd is as good as an alternative, perhaps being more rocky and classically cwm-like, and providing a truly excellent walk. Cwm Tryfan is less immediately appealing, a vast, open valley, following the line of an anticline. It does, however, offer very impressive views of Tryfan and is highly atmospheric. In addition, the shapes of the outcrops of rocks are fascinating and there are a lot to see and plenty of choice of paths.

Photo w4.1 | View from Tryfan's north ridge towards Idwal Cottage.

North Ridge Route

START	▶	A5 NEAR GWERN GOF UCHAF (673 605)
FINISH	●	CIRCULAR ROUTE
TIME	☾	5 HOURS PLUS
GRADE	☉	NAVIGATION ● ● ●
	⌔	TERRAIN ● ● ● ● ●
	✷	SEVERITY ● ● ● ● ●

The best place to begin is at Milestone Buttress (663 602). Here Tryfan's north ridge comes down to earth only metres in from the road, so this route offers stiff, steep scrambling from the very start – though this also means that you gain height and enjoy excellent views quite rapidly (see photo w4.1).

Initially the outcrops, and many of the tumbled blocks, are rhyolitic tuffs of the CCV but very soon the outcrops are all intrusive rhyolite and this remains the case right up onto the start of the summit plateau area. This doesn't mean that the rocks lack interest. The scramble

Photo w4.2 | Siliceous nodules in intrusive rhyolite on north ridge (block is about 2.5 metres high).

Photo w4.3 | Flow-banding in intrusive rhyolite, below south peak summit of Tryfan (block is about 4 metres high).

gives you plenty of opportunity to see the vast variety of rock types within this one category – with plenty of flow-banding and siliceous nodules to be seen (see photo w4.2).

There is no one track to follow and you can choose harder or easier scrambles. In general the easiest route is in the middle, with harder, more exposed routes towards the sides. On the third of the very substantial ledges you come across it's necessary to make a choice on whether to scramble directly further up the ridge; from here the scrambling sections become a bit longer and require a bit more of head for heights.

The alternative is to follow a narrow track round to the left of the ridge, high above Cwm Tryfan, leading you to a gully or cleft on the right. You then scramble up the gully to regain the ridge. The difficulty here is getting past a boulder lodged high up in the cleft. It's not too difficult but does require a little bit of undignified stretching, and heaving. The gully then takes you to the summit ridge and the summit without further difficulty.

Unless you've done it a few times before, the route finding on Tryfan's north ridge and the demands of the scrambling will probably have prevented too close an attention being paid to the rocks, but if you do keep an eye on the rocks you can see some interesting examples of flow-banding and outcrops containing siliceous nodules. At some point you will have crossed back from the intrusive rhyolite to the rhyolitic tuffs of the CCV – the crazy, frost-shattered shapes of boulders on summit area are made of CCV rocks. As you descend you will cross back into the intrusive rhyolite once again, probably near Bwlch Tryfan, or you may cross the boundary more than once as it does depend on the line you take, the boundary between the rocks being rather convoluted at the present-day surface.

Some graphic flow-banding and other features can be seen in intrusive rhyolites on the descent from the summit as you get near the low bwlch (663 592) where the Heather Terrace walk joins the ridge, just before the 'south peak'. The route trends somewhat to the right, away from the crest of the south ridge, as it descends to the blwch (662 589) opposite Glyder Fach's Bristly Ridge.

Both routes meet at this point (663 592) where there are plenty of interesting outcrops to be seen (see photo w4.3). Descend initially towards Llyn Bochlwyd, with the south peak to the left, but as soon as possible bearing left to aim south and then just east of south while dropping down below the south peak, eventually joining the north-eastern end of Bwlch Tryfan (6622 5890). Follow the stone wall south-westwards towards the base of Bristly Ridge.

From here you have a choice of routes, the recommended route turning left to head south-east on the Miners' Track around the head of Cwm Tryfan, or right to return via Cwm Bochlwyd. To carry on along the recommended route, follow the Miners' Track around the

Photo w4.4 | Tryfan (left) and Cwm Tryfan (lower centre and right).

Tryfan

head of the cwm as far as the junction shown on the OS map at 6656 5835. Bear left and follow the track (initially steep and stony) down into Cwm Tryfan – though you may want to look at the prominent rocks just beyond the junction before dropping down into the cwm. These are well-bedded sedimentary rocks, forming a rock step carved by the ice which flowed, from the Migneint ice sheet, over the ridge of the Glyderau further along up the Miners' Track, down into Cwm Tryfan (see Walk 3, Glyder Fach).

There are several tracks which you can follow down the Cwm, the main one being no less interesting than any of the minor side routes. You will pass a wide variety of rock types, including rhyolite with flow-banding, CCV and sedimentary rocks, often forming regularly-shaped outcrops with steeply dipping strata (see photo w4.4).

Eventually you come across a fence that runs west-east, meeting the main track at 671 599. Turn left along the fence until you meet the stile and footpath back (see photo w4.3 and diagram w4.1), at about 669 599, down to Tryfan Bach, Gwern Gof Uchaf and the main road.

Heather Terrace Route

START	▶	A5 NEAR GWERN GOF UCHAF (673 605)
FINISH	●	CIRCULAR ROUTE
TIME	☾	4 HOURS PLUS
GRADE	✱	NAVIGATION ● ● ●
	☁	TERRAIN ● ● ● ●
	✪	SEVERITY ● ● ● ●

This option can also be started from the Milestone Buttress, initially climbing upwards, then heading west from about 450 metres altitude to meet the track to the Heather Terrace. However, it can be hard to work out exactly where to move across and get onto the Heather Terrace and it's all too easy to end up straying on to the steepening south-eastern flanks of Tryfan. The described route is a much easier way to find the Heather Terrace.

Take the track heading just west of south from the road towards Gwern Gof Uchaf farm (and campsite), then follow footpath (shown on OS map) past Tryfan Bach – a popular site for trainee climbers. Above the climbers' crags the track bears off half right between other outcrops, eventually bringing you up to a stile across a fence.

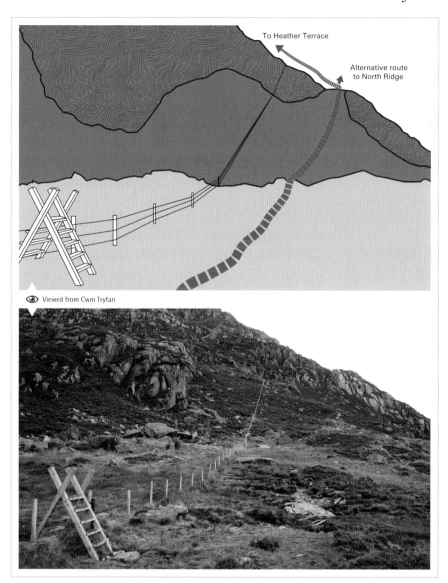

To Heather Terrace

Alternative route
to North Ridge

Viewed from Cwm Tryfan

Diagram w4.1 + Photo w4.5 | Route to the Heather Terrace – follow track on
right of fence to ridge line (reached just after passing through a rock outcrop), then
turn sharp left and follow path up on to the terrace. See diagram w4.1.

Ignore the stile and turn right just before the fence and follow the track heading up to the base of the north ridge (see photo w4.3 and diagram w4.1). After passing through a cleft with outcrops on either side, turn sharp left and follow the track upwards as it heads for the south-eastern face of Tryfan. After rising up steeply for 50 metres or so the track suddenly becomes rather wider, while still rising upwards across the main face.

This is the Heather Terrace and is etched into softer sedimentary rock with outcrops of the Capel Curig Volcanics below you on the left and rhyolite forming the crags rearing up above you on the right. As you ascend you can see the rhyolites in great detail, however the CCV rocks are less easy to study. This is a fantastic walk with truly excellent views to the east and with the presence of crags rising up above you to Tryfan's summit, on the righthand side.

All too soon the Terrace peters out, though conveniently it does so just 20 metres or so below the bwlch between the summit and the south peak, so scrabble up the scree as soon as the rock outcrops end on your right. An optional ascent to Tryfan's summit is fairly easy from here, though it remains a 'hands-on' scramble, especially higher up. To continue the described route join the main route at this point.

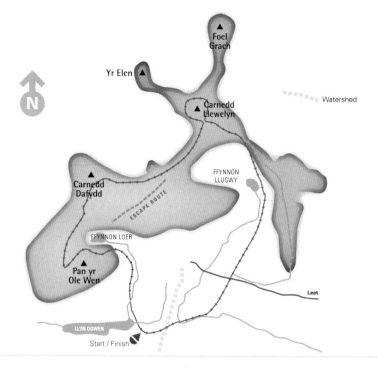

Walk #5 Y Carneddau

START	▶	TRACK SIGNPOSTED TO GLEN DENA (6684 6053)
FINISH	●	CIRCULAR ROUTE
TIME	☻	6 HOURS PLUS
GRADE	☊	NAVIGATION ● ● ● ●
	☁	TERRAIN ● ● ● ●
	☊	SEVERITY ● ● ● ● ● (DUE TO LENGTH AND REMOTENESS)

The Carneddau form a vast area, much of it over 900 metres above sea level. The range is separated from the Glyderau by the glacial trench of Nant Ffrancon/Nant y Benglog to the east and south. But to the north and west, the Carneddau run slowly down towards the sea, or right up to it, forming steep sea cliffs between Penmaenmawr and Conwy. In winter and spring the Carneddau often have a cover of snow while the more westerly mountains are clear.

Y Carneddau

The recommended walk crosses the highest mountains in the range, including Carnedd LLewelyn, which at 1,044 metres is the second highest in Wales, after Snowdon.

This walk is slightly different from the others, in that I point to fewer features on the way, but include a short account of the overall Carneddau volcanic cycle from a vantage point at the north-eastern corner of the summit plateau of Carnedd LLewelyn.

This is a long walk and quite demanding, so it should not be underestimated. I have added a few points where you can visit other nearby summits from Carnedd LLewelyn, but these extras would only really be feasible during the long days of spring and summer, as the basic walk is about all you can reasonably manage in the time available on a winter's day.

The recommended route for the Carneddau follows the classic horseshoe encompassing Pen yr Ole Wen, Carnedd Dafydd and Carnedd LLewelyn. Once you have reached the summit of Pen yr Ole Wen the bulk of the uphill climbing is done and the walk traverses superb, high-level connecting ridges with excellent views in all directions.

From the start point, the track leading from the A5 into a copse of pine trees at the eastern end of Llyn Ogwen, follow the sign towards Glan Dena farm. After crossing the stile, cross Afon Lloer stream as soon as possible to the western side. This can be difficult if in flood, when it is not worth attempting a crossing. Instead, you can keep the stream on the left and follow round the edge of Ffynnon Lloer (see photo w5.1) to the start of the climb up the eastern ridge of Pen yr Ole Wen.

The initial climb up the eastern ridge involves a short scramble, followed by a slog up the ridge, crossing sedimentary rocks, cleaved volcanic tuffs (see photo w5.2) and intrusive dolerites. The views from the cairn, a short distance south-west of the summit of Pen yr Ole Wen, are truly spectacular and are worth a small diversion. The view to the Glyderau on the opposite side of the valley is stunning, presenting a run of cwms and hanging valleys above the valley floor.

Return to the track and follow it along the top of the ridge between Pen yr Ole Wen and Carnedd Dafydd, passing the ancient cairn of Carnedd Fach about halfway, with Fynnon Lloer way below you on the right

Photo w5.1 | Ffynnon Lloer – a glacial lake held behind a rock bar.

Photo w5.2 | Capel Curig volcanic outcrop showing cleavage (ridge up to Pen yr Ole Wen).

From the summit of Carnedd Dafydd, head roughly east along the top of the great crags of Cefn Ysgolion Duon (the 'Black Ladders') – for the best views scramble over the dolerite boulder fields close to the edge, or alternatively skirt the boulders on the right for a much easier progress, but correspondingly less dramatic views.

After about 1.5 km, the ridge narrows with magnificent views down into Cwm Llafar to the north-west and Cwm Llugwy to the east, and with the bulk of Carnedd Llewelyn and its satellite, Yr Elen, to the north; don't neglect here to turn round back towards Carnedd Dafydd for more fine views. Various rock types are crossed as you walk along the narrowish ridge and ascend towards the summit of Carnedd Llewelyn, including welded tuffs and sedimentary rocks. You should reach the flat summit plateau of Carnedd Llewelyn near the summit shelter.

Take a few moments to work out the shape of the plateau and to remember how to get back to this summit shelter later on, as we will walk around the edge of the plateau for the views and a look at the volcanic history of the Carneddau. When ready head just north

Y Carneddau

Photo w5.3 | View north towards Anglesey, from Carnedd LLewelyn.

of west towards the summit tors seen in the middle distance. You will notice that the rocks underfoot soon change to darker colour than those you followed up the flank of Carnedd LLewelyn to the summit shelter. The tors you are heading towards are the same darker colour rocks. This is a basaltic lava and it makes up most of the summit plateau, indeed for all except for the southern corner where you arrived.

When you meet the tors, a view should open up towards Yr Elen. This subsidiary top is well worth a visit, but will add one hour to overall route time. Otherwise, make your way round to the north-eastern corner of the summit plateau to find a good spot to sit with a view over the northern Carneddau (see photo w5.3).

The 1st Eruptive Cycle, the cycle of volcanic activity which produced the LLewelyn Volcanic Group rocks, preceded the eruptions of the main Snowdon Volcanic Group. Essentially, the 1st Eruptive Cycle and the later 2nd Eruptive Cycle were part of the same wider process towards the end of the volcanic activity on the plate boundaries; they took place during a period of some 3.5 million years, though each cycle only took up to a few hundred thousand years to be completed, so there was a longish gap between them. The 1st Eruptive Cycle involved several different centres of eruptions from Conwy in the north-east to near Tryfan and Glyder Fach in the south-west. It produced both lava flows and pyroclastic explosions (tuffs and breccias) at different times in the cycle. 'Intrusive' magma was also inserted in between the still soft volcanic rocks soon after they were laid down.

The first set of eruptions was near present day Conwy, producing rhyolite lavas and rhyolitic ash-flow tuffs (the Conwy Rhyolitic Formation). The erupted material produced rocks up to 1km thick and deposits were spread 12km to the south-west.

Two further sets of eruptions happened at roughly the same time a few kilometres south-west of Conwy, producing the Foel Fras Volcanic Complex (intermediate lavas and tuffs) and the Foel Grach Basalt Formation (basaltic-intermediate lavas). These eruptions were probably associated with the development of a caldera along fissure-vents aligned north-east to south-west. In places the rocks deposited are again up to 1km thick. Another set of eruptions, the Braich tu du Volcanic Formation produced yet more rhyolitic ash-flow tuffs and rhyolites around the same time but further south-west, producing rocks up to 400 metres thick in places.

The final set of eruptions was the biggest, producing the Capel Curig Volcanics (CCV) which outcrop heavily on the Glyderau (Tryfan, Glyder Fach and Gallt yr Ogof) as well as on today's walk on the southern Carneddau. The eruptions took place at four different sites from north (Garnedd Uchaf) to south (Glyder Fach), with the bigger eruptions to the south. The two northern vents were above sea level, while the two to the south were below sea. The rocks produced include rhyolitic tuffs and breccias. In addition rhyolite and dolerite were intruded after each set of eruptions. Well over 25 million cubic metres of magma was erupted or intruded in this last eruptive cycle.

Thus to summarise, the view north and north-west from this end of the summit plateau of Carnedd Llewelyn allows you to cast an eye over the rolling mountain landscape produced by the interplay of volcanic eruption, mountain-building and glaciation. The eruption vents shifted location steadily over the 1st Eruptive Cycle from Conwy, towards and beyond where you now sit, producing the most explosive mix right at the end. The whole series of eruptions probably took many tens or possibly a few hundreds of thousands of years, with short cycles of several months or years of individual eruptions at each centre.

The 2nd Eruptive Cycle, which produced the Snowdon Volcanic Group rocks, occurred probably a couple of million years later, again somewhat further south-west along the same general axis of movement. The Carneddau were later subject to glaciation. The rolling landscape of the Carneddau suggests that cwm glaciation was less intense towards the north and west. The most impressive glacial cwms in the Carneddau are those passed on today's walk (Cwm Lloer and Cwm Llugwy) and also Cwm Dulyn 2 or 3km north-east of where you are sitting.

A trip further on to the northern summit of Foel Grach adds another hour there and back and another 1.5 hours from there to Foel Fras if you want to cover all of the most northerly of Wales' 3,000 foot summits.

5 Y Carneddau

Photo w5.4 | View south to Cwm Llugwy, from Carnedd LLewelyn
– the main track down can be seen on the left of the photo, just to the right of the ridge line.

Return to the summit cairn on Carnedd LLewelyn in the southern corner of the summit plateau to find the route down – note that great care needs to be taken in the mist to get the right track. The walk now continues down the eastern ridge (note that initially the track heads almost due south-east for 100 metres or so before turning east). You descend through rhyolite and rhyolitic breccias until the slope flattens out, where the route swings right to head south-east, and you cross first sedimentary rock and then more CCV breccia. It takes extra effort at the end of a long walk, but if possible leave the track and follow the edge, scrambling over the boulders for the best views (see photo w5.4). You can see the bedding and folds in the rocks across the other side of Cwm Eigiau.

Eventually the CCV outcrops give way to more sedimentary rocks – these being less re-sistant to erosion by ice have resulted in the narrow ridge above Ffynnon Llugwy. The descent to the ridge is a bit steep and requires a careful, but very short, scramble. From the ridge, either drop down at the cairn into Cwm Llugwy and on to the reservoir track and back to the road, or carry on up the narrow ridge edge (a short, steep, exciting but fairly safe scramble) to Pen Llithrig y Wrach (the head of the slippery witch) and then down its blunt nose, eventually picking up a track leading to a leat cutting horizontally across the end of the nose, turn right and follow the leat to the reservoir track, then down to the road (adds 45 minutes).

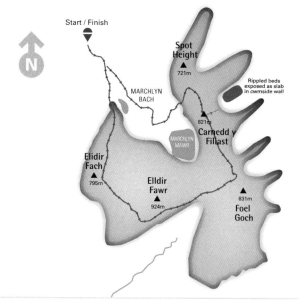

Walk #6 Elidir Fawr

START	▶	CAR PARKING SPACE AT END OF ROAD (597 631)
FINISH	●	CIRCULAR ROUTE
TIME	☾	5 HOURS PLUS
GRADE	⊙	NAVIGATION ● ● ●
	☁	TERRAIN ● ● ● ●
	◉	SEVERITY ● ● ● ● ● (DUE TO REMOTENESS)

Elidir Fawr, or Carnedd Elidir, is the northernmost of Snowdonia's 14 peaks over 3,000 foot in height, and the only one made up of sedimentary, as opposed to volcanic, rocks. It stands, deeply scarred by quarrying, over the villages of Llanberis and Nant Peris, marking the northern end of the glacial trench carved into the Llanberis Pass and the north-western end of the Glyderau Ridge.

The views of the Snowdonia mountain ranges, from the Carneddau, the Glyderau, the Snowdon massif and ranges to the west, are outstanding. To the north, the lowlands around Caernarfon and Bangor and on Anglesey offer a contrasting

Elidir Fawr

view. The walk also brings you close to some very good examples of the Cambrian sedimentary grits and siltstones of this part of central Snowdonia.

This walk is based on a horseshoe round of Carnedd y Filiast, Mynydd Perfedd and Elidir Fawr, with an optional diversion to Foel Goch. It is the only walk in the book which cannot be done as specified with public transport (so I also give details at the end of an alternative walk for those without a car). The walk is not very demanding, but does involve the need to scramble up or along outcrops and cross awkward boulder fields. It goes to some fairly remote spots, and thus is a reasonably serious undertaking.

The walk follows a clockwise horseshoe route over Carnedd y Filiast, Mynydd Perfedd and Elidir Fawr with some steep climbs and some narrowish ridges but should be well within the capabilities of the fit hillwalker. The hills are mainly sedmentary rocks, except for Mynydd Perfedd (the 'central' mountain) which is a microgranite intrusion.

From the parking place, follow the power station tarmac track, passing a slate quarry on the right, and then Marchlyn Bach (now a reservoir connected with the hydroelectric power station in Dinorwig Quarry). After passing through the stone wall (6090 6260) shortly after the lake you can break off left at any time, but it is better to stick to the tarmac for an excellent view of an anticline a bit further on. A crash barrier is provided on the right hand side of the track at a point where you get an unimpeded view over Marchlyn Bach and the cliffs behind it, so you can easily see the anticline. The rocks are outcrops of the Bronllwyd Grits (see photo 5.1).

This spot is also a good place for a view of the relation between rock and relief. Turn round to look at Carnedd y Filiast, noting the wide shallow area halfway up to the summit (seen from a higher perspective in photo 1.8). The shallow area is made up of soft siltstones (Marchlyn Flags), while on either side there are tougher grits (Bronllwyd Grits to the left (north) and Carnedd y Filiast Grits to the right (the summit). You can see how the grits on either side provide innumerable outcrops, while the siltstones are generally covered by vegetation. Then, look back at the crags above Marchlyn Bach and to its left and you see the same pattern repeated. You can also begin to distinguish the different rock outcrops.

Carry on along the winding tarmac road until it splits (6155 6247) and take the left turning which swings round left and drops down slightly. After about 100 metres, swing right off the road and cross the stile over a wire fence on the right; the track ascends diagonally across the slope to the bwlch (col) and two tiny ponds at the bottom of the final slope up to Carnedd y Filiast (the ponds are useful markers if the mist descends and you need to find the track back down to the power station track).

From the bwlch if you wish you can visit 'spot height 721' and its two stone shelters, offering fine views to the north and east.

Continue to the summit of Carnedd y Filiast, preferably using the track close to the edge overlooking Cwm Ceunant (except in windy conditions when a track well away from the edge comes in handy).

As you ascend you can see quite clearly how the cwm has been centred on the weaker Marchlyn Formation siltstones and how the two enclosing arms are formed by the tougher grits on either side (seen from below in photo 7.4).

You can also see the Marchlyn Formation rocks below your feet as you climb, ranging from grey-weathered small blocks (often displaying rough cleavage), via red/brown-weathering smaller rocks, to yet smaller slaty pieces of grey-blue fresher faces. These smaller rocks often also show fine lines of bedding.

However after about 90 metres of ascent the rocks suddenly change, with large grey-weathered outcrops sticking out of the ground. This is the transition to the Carnedd y Filiast Grits. These rocks make up the summit of Carnedd y Filiast and also Elidir Fawr itself.

As the track approaches the outcrops it first swings right and then left, between outcrops to a small col. The main track then swings right again from the col and ascends the large blocks of grits, becoming more and more of a scramble as you get closer to the summit (which can be avoided by following the faint track that leads from the minor col to the eastern side for a much easier route).

There is a deep stone shelter at the summit, but if the weather permits better views are had from sitting on the summit ridge. There are good views of Marchlyn Mawr's dam from here; water is stored in the reservoir and then released to fall down through pipes built inside Elidir Fawr to feed massive hydroelectric turbines, which are also built into a cavern within the mountain near Llyn Peris. Full power is reached within seconds, but the water is also used up quite quickly, so the power station is used when the national grid experiences a sudden load (famously at the end of a football match on the television when everyone switches on their electric kettles). On leaving the turbines the water is released into Llyn Peris and then pumped back up, overnight, into the Marchlyn Mawr reservoir for re-use. Marchlyn Mawr and Marchlyn Bach were both glacial cwms in the ice age.

Carry on along the summit ridge to near its end (to where the awkward boulder field that has to be crossed is at its narrowest), scramble down onto grassy ground, cross the boulders and pick up a track that heads to the right (to avoid another nasty boulder-field). The track then swings back left to aim for a stile crossing a stone wall near the eastern edge of the summit plateau.

When you get close to the stile, break off left to the edge of the crags over Cwm Graianog, some 10 metres or so before the stone wall. From here you get a good view of the massive bedding slabs of the Carnedd y Filiast Grits below you. The large ripples in the beds can be clearly seen (see photos 1.10 and w8.1). Also, it is possible (near where the stone wall reaches the edge) to see where the beds of the grits end and beds of the Graianog Sandstones begin.

Looking closely you should be able to see that the angle of bedding of the sandstones is slightly different to the angle of bedding of the grits. The grits are the final formation in the Cambrian era in this area. In the Ordovician era which followed the Cambrian, central Snowdonia was initially above sea level for many millions of years, so there are no rocks from the early parts of the Ordovician era in this area.

There were, however, some minor earth movements and the Cambrian beds were slightly tilted. Later, in the Ordovician era, the area was once again under sea level and new sedimentary rocks were laid down, starting with the Graianog Sandstones. As the previous beds were now at a slight tilt, the new horizontal beds were laid down at a slight angle to them.

Cross the stone wall and, ignoring the main muddy track, follow the edge of the ridge for the best views of Cwm Graianog and Nant Ffrancon, and also of the slabs of rippled bedding in the Carnedd y Filiast Grits and of the rocky moraines in the cwm (see photos 7.5 and w8.2).

Photo w6.1 | View from near summit on Mynydd Perfedd to Esgair y Ceunant Ridge (centre left).

Photo w6.2 | Elidir Fawr (right) from southern slope of Mynydd Perfedd.

You very soon cross into another rock type – an intrusive volcanic rock, actually microgranite, which forms the summit plateau all the way to Mynydd Perfedd. This is a tough, resistant rock (intruded during the 'Llewelyn Eruptive Cycle') and forms the high, southern sidewall of Cwm Graianog. Carry on towards the summit shelter of Mynydd Perfedd – though you'll probably have to move away from the edge to avoid unpleasant boulder fields as you get nearer to it. (See photo w6.1).

From the flat summit of Mynydd Perfedd, there is an option to carry on along the ridge towards Foel Goch and back. To do this, cross the fence on the right and then drop down to Bwlch y Brecan, heading to the base of Foel Goch. Ignore the steep track up to the summit of Foel Goch, instead keep heading south along the main track towards Y Garn until this track brings you to the unnamed bwlch or col below Y Garn (at about 6270 6020).

Here, cross the fence, and do a 180 degrees U-turn, and start heading slightly east of north, back up towards the summit of Foel Goch on a very easy incline. Keep the fence on your left until you reach the gentle stony col (Bwlch y Cwyion), then bear right for superb views of Y Llymllwyd – another microgranite intrusion. If you have plenty of time a trip out to Y Llymllwyd is highly recommended. Otherwise follow the edge up to the sudden dramatic and unexpected opening up of the land below your feet at summit of Foel Goch. Keep a sharp eye out for the sudden drop just beyond the summit (the sharp edges here could be a hazard in bad or very windy weather). The all-round view is outstanding as the summit of Foel Goch is a bit lower than the surrounding peaks. Drop down west to Bwlch y Brecan on the steep track and head up to Elidir Fawr (see photo w6.2).

Elidir Fawr

Photo w6.3 |

The exhilarating ascent of Elidir Fawr from Bwlch y Brecan.

Otherwise, if you don't want to visit Foel Goch, from the summit shelter on Mynydd Perfedd, descend south-west along the edge of the ridge (overlooking Marchlyn Mawr on the right) towards Elidir Fawr, crossing the fence before it veers right down to the lake. Carry on to a narrow col where you drop down a few metres to pick up the main track coming in (left) from Bwlch y Brecan (at about 6200 6153).

Either follow the track that climbs up always a few feet below the ridge line (see photo w6.3), or keep as close to the crest of the ridge as feasible for the best views. This is a very fine walk/scramble, but care is of course needed. Whichever track you take, don't forget to stop every so often to turn around and enjoy the views down into Cwm Dudodyn, over to Snowdon, Y Garn, Bwlch y Brecan and the Carneddau beyond. During the ice age, glacial ice flowed from Nant Ffrancon, across Bwlch y Brecan and down Cwm Dudodyn into the lower Llanberis Pass.

The walk/scramble up the sharp nose suddenly ends and a wide plateau opens up before you. Follow the well-used track up towards the summit ridge. Not far from the summit, the track takes you up to a small bwlch, where it is possible to study the near vertical beds of the Carnedd y Filiast Grits (see photo 1.8).

Follow the main track (or a scrambling minor track on the crest) to the summit shelter. Once again, I can only say that the views are absolutely magnificent, with a vista of the sea to the north, the Carneddau, the Glyderau and Snowdon ranged around, and also other ranges rolling off in the distance towards the Lleyn Peninsula (see photos w6.4 and w6.5).

Photo w6.4 | View east from Elidir Fawr towards Bwlch y Brecan, Foel Goch and, in the distance, to the Carneddau and Tryfan (centre right).

From the shelter, carry on along the summit ridge to Bwlch Melynwyn. Take great care clambering over the jumbled boulders – this is not the place to break an ankle. There is a track down from the cairned grassy area halfway to the bwlch but if you descend here you miss a good part of the walk along the summit ridge and trade it for a steep slithery stony descent. So, unless you are in a hurry to get off the ridge, ignore this option and carry on along the ridge to the Bwlch Melynwyn farther along the summit ridge.

The beds of the grits cross the line of the summit ridge at a gentle angle so you can see the wide range of beds represented by the Carnedd y Filiast Grits. I have found fossils embedded in the rocks in places along this last section of the ridge. Bwlch Melynwyn is reached at 6095 6120.

If you have the energy, climb up on to the prominence just after Bwlch Melynwyn (6093 6118) for the excellent view down towards the Llanberis Pass and the ranges to the west, then return to the bwlch.

From Bwlch Melynwyn, follow the stony track downwards; it soon swings left to accompany a fence down to the col (where the fence goes off left) between Elidir Fawr and

Elidir Fach. Carry on towards the unremarkable 'summit' of Elidir Fach and, on nearing it, turn right and head slightly east of north down the centre of the ridge towards Marchlyn Bach, joining a tarmac power station road on the left of the ridge just before the lake, then turn left at the junction and back to the parking place.

Car-free option via Esgair y Ceunant

START	▶	LLANBERIS BUS INTERCHANGE STOP (582 599)
FINISH	●	CIRCULAR ROUTE
TIME	◔	6 HOURS
GRADE	◐	NAVIGATION ● ● ● ○ ○
	◓	TERRAIN ● ● ● ● ○
	◑	SEVERITY ● ● ● ● ○

An alternative walk, for those who don't want to drive up to the parking place, is to climb Elidir Fawr via a footpath from near Nant Peris. You can take the bus to Nant Peris and start at the wooden footbridge signposted for camping (606 584), or walk from Llanberis by following the main road to the lay-by at (5985 5870), then follow the public footpath to a footbridge (6036 5825), cross the bridge and follow the footpath to Nant Peris. Cross the road, turn left over a wooden footbridge alongside the road, and then turn immediately right, signposted for camping and also as public footpath (606 584).

From the signpost to the campsite, follow this minor road up, bearing left at junction (right for campsite). At the next junction somewhat higher up, keep straight on (left fork) using stile, then about 250 metres after the stile turn right up the footpath (signed). Follow zigzagging footpath to footbridge at 6085 5955.

Here you have a choice. Either turn left over the footbridge and follow the steep, stony track directly up to Elidir Fawr's summit ridge – this is hard, grinding and unpleasant, so is not recommended despite its apparent popularity. A much nicer route is to keep on along the footpath, shortly crossing a stile and then, after about 100 metres, breaking off right and upwards to the base of the ridge, Esgair y Ceunant.

Then a short but stiff ascent puts you on the ridge and from there on the walk is easy and delightful. Either the rocky ridge or later Bwlch y Brecan are always in view and the gradient is fairly gentle, beckoning you along a great little ridge walk (made of toughened siltstones of

Photo w6.5 | View west from Elidir Fawr towards Moel Eilio, Mynydd Mawr and the Lleyn Peninsula.

the Ordovician era – toughened by the heat and pressure of intruded microgranite forming part of a 'metamorphic aureole').

Where the ridge loses its rocky identity and becomes a grassy slope (and the wire fence bears off right), you need to carry straight on in the same direction across wet grass for another 250 metres, then pick up a narrow track heading left directly to Bwlch y Brecan at an easy gradient. On reaching Bwlch y Brecan, bear left and head towards the ridge leading to Elidir Fawr, reaching a narrow cleft in soft rock at about 620 616. From here you start to climb to the summit via the narrowing ridge. A track stays just below the ridge line on the left, but if it's not too windy the best option is to follow the top of the ridge where possible. The ridge suddenly widens into a plateau area and the last 100 metres of ascent to the summit follows a clear track (except for one spot after about 150 metres on the plateau where the track switches 10 metres to the right).

The views are absolutely magnificent, with a vista of the sea to the north, the Carneddau, the Glyderau and Snowdon ranged around, and also other ranges rolling off in the distance towards the Lleyn Peninsula (see photos w6.4 and w6.5).

Elidir Fawr

You may want to explore a short distance along the rocky summit ridge, but the descent involves returning on the same route to Bwlch y Brecan and on to the start of the steep track up Foel Goch.

Head up straight up the steep stony slope to the summit. Descend southwards along the edge of Cwm Coch until you get a good view of Y Llymllwyd, then bear right to meet the fence at the minor col (at about 6277 6090). Step over the low fence and head just south of south-west until the Esgair y Ceunant Ridge comes into view, then head down to it (aiming for the point where the wire fence begins to run along the ridge).

Follow along the ridge until the complex of stone walls and stiles (at around 6165 5976). Cross to the left using the stile a few metres in advance of the stone wall and then turn sharp right around sheepfolds to follow the stone wall along to the point where the ridge suddenly becomes steeper. From here bear left following close to the nose of the ridge, but picking a route down through outcrops to below the waterfall marked on the OS map. At about 6150 5910 (a bit below the waterfall) you can get a reasonable view from steep grass/bracken covered slopes (but take care – don't try to get too close). Then head roughly west, slowly losing height, across boggy ground in places and using appropriate gates to cross any fences. Aim for the stile and footpath at the boundary of access land (at about 6066 5913) and back to Nant Peris and Llanberis.

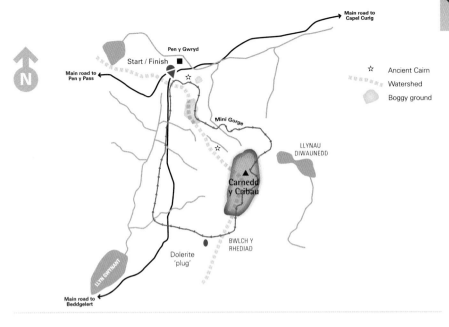

Walk #7 Carnedd y Cribau

START	▶	LAY-BY OPPOSITE THE PEN Y GWRYD HOTEL (6601 5575)
FINISH	●	CIRCULAR ROUTE
TIME	◕	5 HOURS PLUS
GRADE	⊙	NAVIGATION ● ● ●
	◔	TERRAIN ● ● ●
	⊗	SEVERITY ● ● ●

To the south-east of Snowdon lies a low, flattish-topped, 'X'-shaped ridge, with outstanding views of the Snowdon Horseshoe, the glacial breaching point at Pen y Pass, and along the glacial trench of Nant Gwynant to western ranges of mountains, as well views as towards the hills around Blaenau Ffestiniog and to the Migneint.

The maximum height on the ridge is lower than 700 metres. Except for Bwlch y Rhediad (the col between Carnedd Cribau and Moel Meirch which drops to 375 metres) the dips between the highpoints are rarely more than 50 metres lower down and thus do not really earn the label of bwlch (col). However, the terrain is complex with numerous knolls, dips, boggy flats, rock outcrops, small and medium crags, and small lakes – many hardly more than large puddles. To the southern end of the ridges there are also many larger lakes, some, such as Llyn Edno, of stunning beauty. The going can be hard, especially so at the northern end of the ridge, with its boggy, tussocky ground and twisting tracks. Gaiters are essential if you want to avoid wet feet.

Despite the hard going, all this adds up to an excellent area for walking, often below cloud level while the higher ranges 'have their hats on'. When the hats are off, it's also a good place to study the landscape of Snowdon, the Glyderau and other ranges.

There's also a wide range of geological features and rocks to be seen. However, this is an area probably best avoided in the mist, as it requires very good map-reading skills to compare the map to the actual scenery – one knoll or outcrop can look very much like another. There is a fence running along the main ridge line for much of its length, though working out where to get off could be a problem. Fortunately Bwlch y Rhediad (6665 5239) is fairly well-defined. (Relying on the fence north of Carnedd y Cribau to guide you down is not advised as it crosses a stream which can be difficult to get across when in spate, and even if crossed, you are later dumped in very wet ground east of Llyn Lockwood.)

The recommended walk heads for the summit of Carnedd y Cribau via a small gorge that, on closer examination, turns out to be located a major faultline and part of the Snowdon caldera. There is a variety of fascinating rock types to be seen on the summit ridge as well as great views.

The detailed directions given for the walk will require some experience with using a map and compass for 'micro-navigation'. However, it is not necessary to visit all the points specified. For an easier route ignore the details and, from the start point at Pen y Gwryd, simply head roughly in the direction of the summit, picking a route across the easier ground (there is no track to follow) and from the summit stick as close as feasible to the fence all the way along the ridge to Bwlch y Rhediad and there pick up an obvious track (public footpath) down into Nant Gwynant. You may miss the best examples, but you can see other examples of the features of the main rock types as you pass along.

Photo w7.1

Ancient cairn passed on the described walk, with Snowdon horseshoe in the background.

Start from the bus lay-by opposite the Pen y Gwryd Hotel and head south along the road for about 250 metres to a stile on the left and head south-east, uphill for about 80 metres or so until the slope shallows out. When you gain the flatter ground, head for the rock outcrops and the high point at about 6630 5500. These outcrops are the Lower Rhyolitic Tuffs (LRT), the major rocks output during the collapse of the caldera around the Snowdonia area.

From the high point of these outcrops head indirectly, using slightly higher ground, towards a prehistoric cairn at 6664 5468[1] (marked on the OS map just to the right of the final 'n' of 'Cairn'). The higher ground appears as several small ring contours on the map and takes you most of the way to the cairn, but some boggy low ground needs to be crossed.

Make use of this approach to identify the stream you need to follow later (in the instructions of the next paragraph). It is the farther left (more northerly) of the two streams you can

---

[1] Note that there is another ancient cairn marked on the OS map at 6648 5540, but there is nothing observable at this location, although there are remains of a cairn nearby at 6640 5542 (i.e. just about at the 'a' of 'Cairn'). This site is just north-east of the bulge in the 340m contour line just below the 'a'. If you visit this site, the bulge turns out to be a rock outcrop and is intrusive rhyolite with some interesting examples of flow-banding. I have left visiting this cairn out of the walk because of the possible confusion over its location.

see coming down the mountainside towards you. The cairn you are aiming for is below the right-hand (more southerly) stream, so head towards it.

The cairn is fairly small and is really only visible from the surrounding high points, and, unusually, not from any low points (see photo w7.1). Perhaps significantly the site, if not the cairn itself in its present state, is visible from the Snowdon massif. All this makes its role in the landscape even more inscrutable, but no less evocative.

From the cairn head 200 metres north-east, following a stony track at the bottom of the slope towards the farther left (northerly) of two small streams coming down the hill, aiming to reach the stream at about 6680 5467 and then follow it uphill into a small gorge cut into the rock (more intrusive rhyolite).

At around 6695 5454, the gorge becomes a narrow cleft for a short time. From around here clamber up to the top of the rocky knoll, high up on the left (6706 5455). The gorge and the knoll mark the last of the intrusive rhyolite rocks at this point, and above here we are enter an area of softer sedimentary rocks which have been eroded into a much more subdued shape, a low hoggy bowl as opposed to the knobbly shape of the more resistant volcanic rocks on either side of the gorge. Before leaving the top of the knoll, turn around for a wonderful view of the Snowdon Horseshoe and Pen y Pass, where you can see very clearly the narrow, deep trench cut when the outflow glacier of the Migneint ice sheet overran the pre-glacial watershed (see photo w7.2).

Photo w7.2 | Ancient fault line, northern edge of Snowdon caldera, approximate line of volcanic fissure-vent, Pen y Pass glacial breaching point, minor gorge and tiddly little stream.

The tiny stream you have followed has cut a small gorge, suggesting that this was once the course of glacial meltwater, under great pressure and containing masses of boulders and pebbles, sufficient to batter a deep gorge. However, there are deeper causes for a deep stream on this particular line. The stream follows the line of a major fault and also the line of main Snowdon volcanic caldera (and thus also a major area for eruptions during the Lower Rhyolitic phase).

Another intriguing aspect of this apparently inconspicuous little stream is not so evident from this viewpoint, but can be seen on the map (and is also very noticeable from the early stretches of the Miners' Track on Snowdon, soon after it leaves Pen y Pass). Both this stream, and the other, southerly, stream to your left (seen near the second cairn), flow down the hill, but, just above the cairn, perform a sharp ninety degree turn to the right and head off, just east of north, to dump their waters in Dyffryn Mymbyr and on to the sea at Conwy. Yet only one or two hundred metres beyond the point where the streams turn sharply to the right, another stream rises, taking its waters down to Nant Gwynant and the sea at Porthmadog.

In all probability one would expect these two streams to continue straight down to Nant Gwynant, but for some reason they have been diverted to the right and Dyffryn Mymbyr, almost certainly at the end of the ice age.

It means that the modern watershed runs from Pen y Gwryd, roughly following the line you followed to the second cairn, then carries on up to the summit ridge further west than the more southerly stream (over to your left now as you look towards Pen y Pass), rather than on the crest of the hill (to your right) as you would expect.

Turn back towards the summit ridge, but head half-left, avoiding the shallow (boggy) basin at the head of the stream, aiming to meet a fence coming up the hillside from the left. The rock outcrops you encounter as you get closer to the fence are dolerite.

The col, Bwlch Rhiw'r Ychen (fence junction at 6764 5423) marks the continuation of the major fault followed by the stream as seen earlier on, and indeed the same fault carries on further eastwards, underneath the hour-glass-shaped lakes Llynau Diwaunydd, seen below, and the valley beyond.

This fault also marks the boundary of the Snowdonia caldera, which swings gently right here to head south-west, paralleling the direction of the Carnedd y Cribau Ridge.

Turn up towards the summit following the fence, crossing dolerite, sedimentary rocks, basalt and finally more intrusive rhyolite (of which there is a very good outcrop left of the fence just before the final summit knoll). The final dip, and its short cliff, is the site of a small fault which runs across the ridgeline.

The summit area is also rhyolite, and indeed the rhyolite carries on for another 500 metres as you descend the ridge to the south until the LRT starts to crop out once again. The boundary between the LRT and the rhyolite runs irregularly down along the ridge and is displaced by a lot of faults, so depending on the exact line you take down the wide ridge, you may be at any one time be walking past either type of rock.

Several faults, trending roughly north-west to south-east, cut across the ridge line. These faults are responsible for the stepped nature of the ridge as it descends, with transverse outcrops producing small cliffs that have to be negotiated (and which also provide plenty of opportunities to study the rocks). One such fault was passed just before the summit, marked by the cliff face of the final few metres up to the summit, as mentioned above.

You will cross several more faults on the descent (they cross the fence line at roughly 675 534, 674 530, 673 531 and 672 530). Each fault is marked by a small cliff followed by a low, flat area. (Two more faults are crossed lower down at about 668 523, just before Bwlch y Rhediad, producing the last cliff face to be negotiated).

I suggest a particular line down the ridge to Bwlch y Rhediad, though it may be difficult to follow the precise instructions. This is not important, any general line will do. The route I recommend keeps to the left of the fence for half the descent of the ridge crossing the cliff marked fault lines, then switches to the right of the fence to seek a path through crags which run start to roughly parallel the ridge, rather than cut across it.

Descend with the fence on your right, negotiating the occasional rock step, picking a line to suit ease of progress (it sometimes makes sense to move away from the fence to cross boggy areas).

Near 6753 5330 you reach a stile at the head of another rock step. Turn half left, away from the stile, and head down through a grassy gap in the crags. These crags represent the second of the transverse faults to be crossed on the descent from the summit. About half-way down the slope, the crags on your right open out and by going round to the right at the bottom of the cliff face you can see amazing varieties of 'flow-banding' in the rhyolite (6743 5323) – see photo w7.3 & w7.4. You can see some where the lower bands are all lined up horizontally, but with jumbled (or 'brecciated') lumps above (see photo 4.8). This happens when a new flow breaks up the higher bands of a previous flow, but leaves the lower bands undisturbed. The intensity and variety of flow-banding you can see is highly impressive.

The rhyolitic rocks around here may be rare rhyolitic lavas (intrusive rhyolite that broke through the surface to become extrusive rhyolite). The presence of rhyolite, whether intrusive or extrusive, means that we are very close to where the magma rose through fault lines (see photo w7.5).

About half-way across the flat area at the bottom of the cliffs, Bwlch Maen Pig (still on the left of the fence – sometimes well away from the fence picking out a route using the slightly higher rock outcrops to avoid boggy areas nearer the fence), the rocks are clearly

Photo w7.3 (top) | Brecciated flow-banding in intrusive rhyolite (width of field of view – 1m).

Photo w7.4 (middle) | Disturbed flow-banding in intrusive rhyolite.

Photo w7.5 (bottom) | Breccia in intrusive rhyolite (outcrop about 3m high).

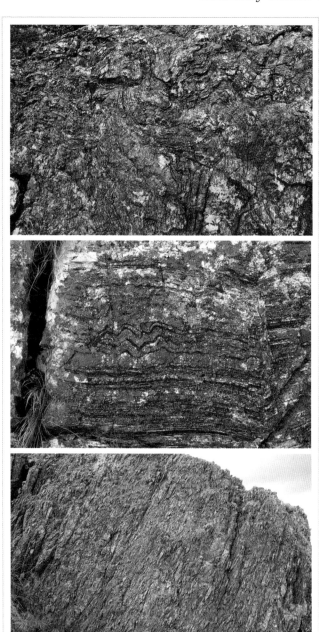

Carnedd y Cribau

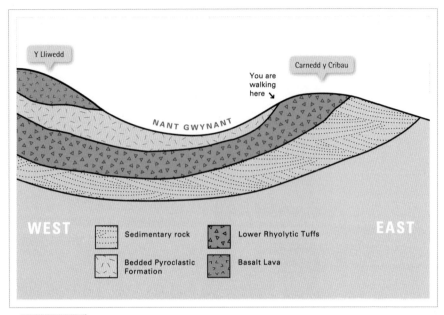

Y Lliwedd

Carnedd y Cribau

You are walking here ↘

NANT GWYNANT

WEST

Sedimentary rock

Lower Rhyolytic Tuffs

Bedded Pyroclastic Formation

Basalt Lava

EAST

Diagram w7.1 | Cross section of geology, southern end of Carnedd y Cribau Ridge.

different, lighter in colour and with no flow-banding to be seen. These are more outcrops of the LRT.

Descend another cliff face caused by a transverse fault (at about 6723 5305), then move towards the fence, crossing it (no stile) to the right hand side (at about 6710 5295) just before a steep rise in the ridge (if you choose to carry on over the rise beside the fence the dark basaltic rocks referred to in the next paragraph can be seen lower down the hillside on the right).

Aim directly away from the fence into a gap between crags on either side. A few metres down, the gap swings left to parallel the ridge, guiding you down between more crags on either side. As you carry on down this gap, on the right hand side, you will start to see much darker rocks that are clearly laid out in beds – these are outcrops of the Bedded Pyroclastic Formation (BPF) (see photo w7.6).

The crags on the left are still in the LRT, so here you are walking along the boundary between two different rock formations. Here there are no transverse faults that earlier on produced the transverse cliff steps. Instead the underlying succession of rocks is exposed in the gap between the crags which parallel the ridge, rather than cut across it. Older LRT rocks (here 're-worked' and deposited as sedimentary rocks) are higher up on your left, and the younger BPF rocks are lower down on the left.

Photo w7.6

Bedded pyroclastic formation outcrop (outcrop is about 2.5m high).

It may seem confusing that by descending you can cross from older to younger rocks. But this is explained by the fact that this ridge is a remnant of an 'up-fold' from a syncline running roughly along the line of the Nant Gwynant valley. Earth movements have folded the rocks and subsequent erosion has exposed different rocks at the surface, so that sometimes tougher older ones (LRT) stick up above slightly softer younger ones (BPF). See diagram w7.1.

Photo w7.7 | View north towards Bwlch y Rhediad and Carnedd y Cribau, showing medieval Cistercian boundary bank and ditch to left of modern wire fence (note – photo taken from lower slopes of Cerrig Cochion looking back towards Carnedd y Cribau).

Carnedd y Cribau

Photo w7.8 | Dolerite 'plug' intruded into sedimentary rock and now standing proud (view from Bwlch y Rhediad to southern flanks of Snowdon).

So, on this low mountain, the actual landscape is a complex mix of factors: the nature of the rocks, they way they have been laid down and the variety of ways they were later moulded into new shapes. It can be seen from our walk along the ridge, that the complex shaping of the ridge is directly related to the type of rock, to the presence of underlying faults and weaknesses in the earth's crust, as well as to earth movements and folding, and of course to the power of glaciation.

Continue down to the Bwlch y Rhediad (6665 5239). Look out for the ancient boundary ditch and bank that runs across the lower slopes on the bwlch, continuing up the other side. This is probably the boundary marker of the medieval Cistercian estate at Nanhwynain (Nant Gwynant) which extended to the ridgeline along this entire ridge (see photo w7.7).

There is no point in looking for the ancient cairn marked on the OS map at 6652 5237 to the left of the path shortly after it starts to descend from the Bwlch as only a tiny, inconspicuous pile of stones marks it (though the stones rest on a low, earth-covered mound visible from the south). More interesting, a hundred or so metres to the south-west of the cairn is a large rocky knoll (6640 5232), the result of a dolerite intrusion (see photo w7.8). Weather permitting it makes a good place to sit atop for a cup of tea and some contemplation before descending. Return to the footpath and descend towards Nant Gwynant.

Cross the main road and continue down to minor road at 6563 5283, turn right to walk back up to the start point.

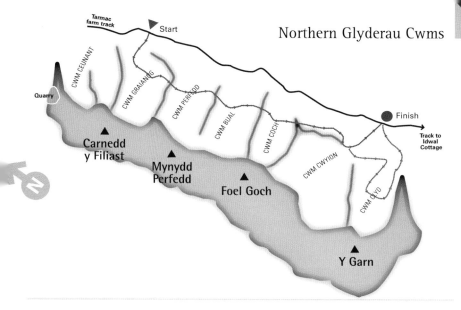

Walk #8 Northern Glyderau Cwms

START	▶	IDWAL COTTAGE CAR PARK AND BUS STOP (6490 6038)
FINISH	●	CIRCULAR ROUTE
TIME	☾	5 HOURS PLUS
GRADE	⊙	NAVIGATION ●
	⬤	TERRAIN ● ● ● ●
	⊗	SEVERITY ● ● ● ●

The line of glacial corries along the northern arm of the Glyderau ridge is impressive when seen from the Carneddau, from the road between Idwal Cottage and Bethesda, or looking down from the ridge above. However, the best way to appreciate these glacial features is to get up inside the cwms and to walk from one to the other.

This is a very different walk to most mountain walks, traversing almost directly along the Glyderau Ridge at thresholds of its line of glacial cwms.

For the described route, I suggest starting the high level part of the walk with Cwm Graianog. It is possible to start with Cwm Ceunant, but the only route I have found from Ceunant into Graianog is over and down a steep ridge with very unpleasant and uneven ground, with lots of heather hiding deep holes – though there may well be a track that I haven't found. The walk is best done north to south to save the highlight, the airy traverse from Cwm Coch to Cwm Cwyion, for the last leg of the high level part of the walk.

I describe the outward route along a minor road, but you could combine the walk along the cwm thresholds with a traverse of the summit ridge. For a much tougher walk, but a very rewarding one indeed, go in reverse, starting at Cwm Cwyion and walk to Cwm Graianog, ascending to the summit of Carnedd y Filiast on the very rocky northern arm of the cwm and returning along the summits.

This walk offers a wholly different perspective on this fine mountain range, offering an intimate glimpse of the features of several glacial cwms as well as providing excellent views.

From Idwal Cottage follow the old road roughly northwards to about 6310 6330 and then strike steeply uphill picking a line between boulders. You want to aim to reach the stone wall just below the threshold of the inner cwm at about 6290 6310, near a gorge cut by the stream through the rocky moraine sitting on the threshold. The cwm is a mass of rocky blocks strewn everywhere – though in fact there is a lot of pattern in their distribution as most are part of moraines left at late stages in the ice age as the cwm glacier slowly retreated as temperatures warmed up (see photos 7.5 and w8.1). If you have time and energy it is worth exploring some of the moraines, otherwise allow your view to move upwards to the great slabs of the Carnedd y Filiast Grits.

Photo w8.1

Cwm Graianog – rocky moraine on threshold of inner cwm (note sheep fold, lower left).

The cwm is quite narrow and very steep all around, creating a very atmospheric spot, especially perched on the edge of the threshold of the cwm overlooking the great glacial trench of Nant Ffrancon (see photos 1.10 and w8.1, and diagram w8.1).

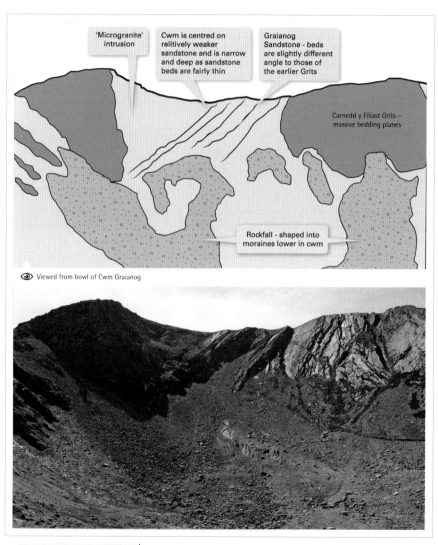

'Microgranite' intrusion

Cwm is centred on relitively weaker sandstone and is narrow and deep as sandstone beds are fairly thin

Graianog Sandstone - beds are slightly different angle to those of the earlier Grits

Carnedd y Filiast Grits – massive bedding planes

Rockfall - shaped into moraines lower in cwm

Viewed from bowl of Cwm Graianog

Diagram w8.1 + Photo w8.2 | Cwm Graianog – slabs of bedding in the Carnedd y Filiast Grits to the right, with beds of Graianog Sandstones in middle (at slightly different angle of tilt); and microgranite intrusion on the left; cwm has developed with its centre at the slightly relatively weaker sandstones.

Northern Glyderau Cwms

Photo w8.3 | Cwm Perfedd and Cwm Bual: separated by low, blunt ridge made up of soft sedimentary rocks, with hard microgranite forming steep side wall, top left, of Mynydd Perfedd.

If you look closely you can see that the beds (of sandstones) visible at the rim of the upper cwm, just to the left of the big slab, are at a slightly different angle to the beds of the grits on the right. These are known as the Graianog Sandstones and were laid down in the Ordovician era, while the grits are Cambrian in age. There was a big time gap (more than 50 million years) between the time the grits and the sandstones were laid down. During this time the area was above sea level and there were some earth movements which tilted the Cambrian grits slightly. So when the Ordovician sandstones were later laid down the beds were at a smaller angle to the beds of the grits. The earth movements that turned all the beds to their present angle of 45 degrees or more came much later (during the mountain-building period responsible for the bulk of Snowdonia's mountain scenery).

A third rock type is also present in the cwm. This is an intruded rock, microgranite, forming the side wall to the left (south). The Cambrian grits and the microgranite are tougher than the sandstones, so the cwm has developed with its centre on the sandstone, a comparative weakness. The result is a long, narrow cwm with high back and side walls, unlike the next two we will meet, which are broad and shallow, with a low back wall and a rounded hump between them rather than a sharp steep nose or arête.

Photo w8.4 | Cwm Cwyion from Y Llwmllwyd cut into beds of sedimentary and volcanic rocks below the pointed summit of Y Garn (Pitts Head Tuffs). Note tiny lake, surrounded by boggy patch, behind moraines (centre left).

To carry on, head up onto the moraine to the south which merges into the arm separating Cwm Graianog from Cwm Perfedd and then contour round over a steep grassy slope into Perfedd. You should come out about 50 metres above two isolated erratic blocks (shown as one block on the OS map at 6299 6238); from here you can see what looks like a path running up from the floor of Cwm Perfedd to the unnamed arm separating it from Cwm Bual. Contour round to pick up the bottom of this feature that, on getting closer, turns out to be a boundary ditch. Follow it to the top of the arm where you can stop for an overview of both cwms (see photos 7.6 and w8.3).

Plenty of moraines are easily distinguishable on the cwm floors. The cwms are unusual in shape with low back walls and side arms (in softer sedimentary rocks) while to the north (below Mynydd Perfedd) and south (Yr Esgair, below Foel Goch) the side arms are much higher – this is because Mynydd Perfedd is made up of tough intrusive microgranite, while Yr Esgair and the summit of Foel Goch are made of sedimentary rock which has been toughened by the intrusion of more microgranite and rhyolite further south at Y Llymllwyd.

Northern Glyderau Cwms

Pick up the track descending from Bwlch y Brecan below Yr Esgair which contours round into Cwm Coch at about an altitude of 450 metres (near a stone wall). This is another deep and narrow cwm, carved into the junction between the toughened sedimentary rock and the intrusive microgranite and rhyolite.

The path continues on round the lower slopes of Y Llymllwyd on a narrow track halfway down the slope. The views here are just fantastic. Eventually the track brings you into Cwm Cwyion, at the lowest point of a gorge at around 6374 6048 (just above the stone wall shown on the OS map). From here you can descend to Yr Hafod hostel and then back along the road to Idwal Cottage. Alternatively, ascend 50 metres into Cwm Cwyion, crossing the stream above the gorge, heading up as far as interest and energy takes you (see photo w8.4).

Cwm Cwyion is the first cwm encountered on the walk that has a 'lake', but it hardly ranks among Snowdonia's most beautiful – for all that the atmosphere within the cwm's enclosing arms, and the unusual perspective on the popular peak of Y Garn, makes it worth the effort to climb some way up into the cwm. When you've seen enough, drop back down towards the gorge, then break off right and head to the stone wall and follow it round below Pinnacle Crag.

If you want to visit Cwm Clyd, scramble up the track that you meet after the crags (shown on the OS map and which eventually ascends Y Garn's northern ridge), breaking off when you reach the level of the cwm, and then descend on a track alongside the outlet stream.

To return to Idwal Cottage, follow the stone wall until you can cut across to Idwal Cottage above the glacial step of Pen y Benglog.

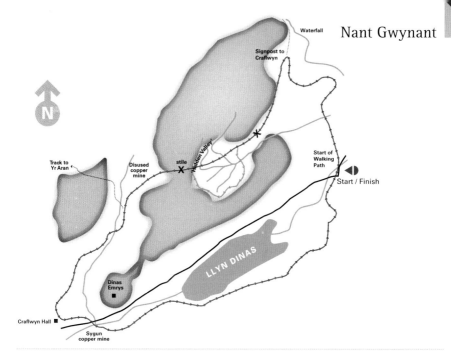

Walk #9 Nant Gwynant

START	▶	WATKIN PATH/CWM YR HAFOD, CAR PARK AND BUS STOP (627 506)
FINISH	●	CIRCULAR ROUTE
TIME	☾	4 – 5 HOURS PLUS
GRADE	⊙	NAVIGATION ● ●
	☁	TERRAIN ● ●
	✪	SEVERITY ● ●

Snowdon is a mountain of vast contrasts, from the rocky grandeur of the Snowdon Horseshoe and Cwm du'r Arddu, the deep gash through the earth that is the Llanberis Pass, the remoteness of the upper reaches of Cwm Glas Mawr, the roller coaster mountainscape of the foothills to the north, the vast sloping moorlands of the western flank to the rough, hilly landscape of Snowdon's southern side along the stunningly beautiful valley of Nant Gwynant.

Much of Nant Gwynant is well known to the visitor – especially famous views of the mountains framing Llyn Gwynant, and the start of the Watkin Path, with its delightful woods and waterfalls. The surrounding slopes between the start of the Watkin Path and Beddgelert have traditionally offered only limited access to the walker, but this area is now nearly all access land and opens up some hidden scenic gems as well as displaying some amazing rock types.

In this walk we explore some of the scenic highlights from that little-known area. It provides a relatively low level walk (reaching a maximum height of about 300 metres) but one which offers the walker a quite different aspect of Snowdon. Apart from the start along the Watkin Path, the crowds are absent and, despite being low down, there is a feeling of isolation and remoteness.

Rather than the lakes and popular paths of the main Snowdon tracks, this walk crosses low hummocky hills and hidden valleys. All this happens quite close to the main Nant Gwynant valley with its motor traffic, but feeling entirely apart from it. The summit of Snowdon itself is not visible. Instead the southern peak of Yr Aran looms above the walker here. Yr Aran looks from the summit of Snowdon like a minor bump, but from here it appears in the guise of a real mountain (and the walk offers an option of ascending Yr Aran).

Commence at the start of the Watkin Path, and follow the track up through woodland. Rising steadily, pass through three gates. Shortly after the third gate the path does a sharp loop around some earthworks. This is part of an incline used to lower slate from the quarry high up in Cwm Llan. You can see the lowest part of the incline to the right below the path as it heads towards the farm buildings.

Carry on along the path which leaves the woods, swings round to the left, and emerges above the stream, Afon Cwm Llan, as it tumbles out of a wide bowl that opens up before you as you follow the path round a rocky prominence.

A wide waterfall draws the attention as the stream pours out of a narrow gap between enclosing mountain arms (behind which Cwm Llan opens up). To the left of the waterfall you can see a straight line running down the hill – the upper part of the incline.

As you follow the path as it winds round the bowl, you can see more of the incline (here almost a level tramway rather than an incline) cutting across the bowl and crossing the path as you head up it. You can turn left, following the tramway to a fence (with gate) just before

Photo w9.1 | The waterfall next to the Watkin Path, near the signpost to Craflwyn.

a rocky knoll named Castell (or castle) on the map. Pass through the gate and then carry on a few metres to peer down the hillside as the tramway again becomes a precipitous incline heading to the farm buildings below.

Return to the Watkin track and continue to follow it round the bowl until the point where the incline crosses the path at the bottom of the crags (a short distance before you reach the waterfall). Here you should see a notice pointing left (south-west) to Craflwyn along a grassy track below the crags (6224 5151).

Before starting out along the path, take in the scenery. Above you are the hard volcanic rocks of the Lower Rhyolitic Tuffs (LRT), the main Snowdon volcanic eruptions. It is this tough rock which forms the arms which enclose Cwm Llan, further up the Watkin Path, channelling the waters of Afon Cwm Llan through a narrow gap in a foaming waterfall (see photo w9.1). The bowl is underlain by the relatively softer Bedded Pyroclastic Formation (BPF), basaltic lavas, tuffs and sedimentary rocks.

The BPF is less resistant than the LRT and has been eroded into the bowl. The crags enclosing the lower part of the bowl (including Castell) around which you walked to enter the bowl are intrusive or extrusive rhyolite, again a tougher rock. The rhyolite thus forms a rim over the main valley beyond, and enclosing the bowl.

Nant Gwynant

The interplay of rock types is the key to understanding the shape of the area that this walks covers, with the line of rhyolite forming a lip that hides the lower land from the Nant Gwynant valley.

Head south-west up the grassy track pointing to Craflwyn. The LRT crags on the right get closer as you go further up the path, starting to loom over you. Then the rhyolite crags on the left also move nearer to you. Closing in from either side, the crags guide you towards a stile over a stone wall (6214 5105). Cross the stile and carry on in the same general direction – from around here the route to Craflwyn is guided by small, black-topped signposts every few hundred metres.

The path now squeezes through rearing crags on either side forming a gorge that rather unexpectedly leads you into a low, wide 'hidden valley', ringed by higher ground.

You can either follow the black-topped signposts and carry straight on (note however that the signposted path follows slightly higher ground to the right of the track shown on the OS map), or follow a slightly more convoluted and correspondingly more scenic route.

To do this, having passed through the gorge, leave the track half-left heading towards a stream, cross the stream a few metres before a small (but noisy) waterfall near some remains of a stonewall and then follow a very faint and twisting track towards the higher ground on the left. Keep heading higher until you see a stone wall and then bear right to follow the top of the higher ground, keeping the stone wall fifty metres or so to your left. After a couple of hundred metres, the high ground peters out near the stone wall. Drop down slightly and bear half-right across a boggy shallow section, then pick up more high ground, heading towards the highest point in the distance. The rocks forming these high points are all rhyolite, and part of the same ridge as seen back at Castell.

From the high point (at about 6143 5022) you get superb views down into Nant Gwynant as well as an overview of the hidden valley (see photo w9.2).

Either from that high point (or if following the signposts after crossing two small streams) it is a time to stop and look around. The hidden valley is wide and shallow. Its stream is drained to the right of the narrow gorge through which you entered the valley.

This structure is a reflection of the underlying geology. The rim of higher ground above Nant Gwynant is made of rhyolite. The floor of the valley is in the BPF, again producing the shallower ground. The higher ground on the other side of the valley (above the signposted track) is more rhyolite, though the LRT forms the main crags higher up.

If following the signposts, they will take you straight to the stile at 6141 5069. If following the ridgeline, then from the high point, reach the stile by following the nearby stone wall that heads north (the stile is invisible until the very last moment so don't despair).

Photo w9.2 | The 'hidden valley' from the high point in its south-eastern corner.

Cross the stile and follow the signposts past a couple of small ridges and intervening shallow areas. There is a small rise, but this is the highest point on the walk. The rocks underfoot here are BPF.

Carry on along the track. After a couple of hundred metres, you will see what is clearly a waste tip from a mine ahead of and to the right of the track. As you approach the waste tip the rocks become quite different and repay careful examination. Here we are back into the rhyolite, but it is quite different from any other rocks we have so far looked at with very intense but broken flow-banding.

As you approach the waste tip, look above you at the crags and below your feet to the rocks you are walking on to see examples of this. At about 6105 5061 you cross a 'pavement' of this intensely busy rock. The best example is a small crag about ten metres above the path just before this pavement – look up to the right. This crag is worth clambering up to (with care) to look closely at the intricate patterns in the rocks (see photo w9.3).

Continuing along the track you approach a ruin (about 6100 5056), part of the extensive copper mine works in this valley. You can go up the valley (with very great care as there are unguarded pits, hidden streams and other hazards) to observe some of the mine workings which exploited minerals in this seam which runs through the rhyolite outcrop where it

Nant Gwynant

Photo w9.3 | Quartz veins in rhyolite, near disused copper mines, Cwm y Bleiddiaid.

bounds the LRT and BPF formation above and to the side. Otherwise, carry on downhill along the clear track.

If you want to ascend Yr Aran instead of going on to Craflwyn, look out for a faint grassy track (6098 5043) that swings away to the right. Follow this twisting track to a gate at about 6053 5058. Then ascend by the stream, first on its left and then on its right, to the rocky prominence above a waterfall at about 6033 5072, then either follow a track up Cwm yr Hyrddod on its left-hand side, or strike out left to hit the ridge near Craig Wen, then turn right and follow the ridge to the summit of Yr Aran. To return to the start point, descend Yr Aran along its east ridge, pick a line between crags (to descend to the footpath marked on the OS map from Bwlch Cwm Llan) either at about 6150 5156 (where the stone wall turns right) heading straight down to avoid a quarry to the right, or go further along the ridge (taking care to avoid crags of Clogwyn Brith on the right) aiming to meet an old tramway track (marked on the map) just east of the footpath (at about 6200 5185).

If you don't want to ascend Yr Aran, to continue with the walk to Craflwyn follow on down the signposted track, passing into the LRT. After a gate, turn sharp right to ford the stream and then sharp left, following the signposts which lead you roughly south-west. The rocks from here on are mainly LRT and rhyolites, very similar to the rocks you've seen so far on the walk.

About 500 metres after fording the stream, and after crossing a nose of higher rocky ground (at about 6024 4977), look up to the ridgeline above. At the bottom of the steep slope, you can see the 'intake' wall marking farmland from moorland. This wall roughly follows the boundary between the BPF, producing flatter land, and the LRT which produces the steep slope (though the top of the ridge and Yr Aran are made of sedimentary rocks). The difference in vegetation is also clear, with rough heather on the rhyolitic LRT rocks.

A stone wall now comes close to the path on the left and crosses it (at about 6024 4976). The stone wall then heads up to a crag on the right and ends there forming a V-shaped sheepfold. Follow the track round to the left, with the crags on the right hidden by vegetation for a further 100 metres or so until you see some rocks, splitting on joints, close to the path on the right. If you scramble up to look at the fresh faces (un-weathered) you will see that these are dark, almost black, rocks. This is a basalt lava outcrop. Further round to the right you can see flow-banding in the lava.

Return to the track, head for and cross a stile and immediately after that a stream, and then carry on for about 150 metres until you meet one of the signposts. Look at the left side of the signpost and it should have a red arrow pointing in the direction in which you have been heading. From here the black signposts are replaced by red, green or yellow ones as this is now the National Trust Craflwyn estate. Turn sharp left here and follow the red signposts against the direction the arrow indicates. After five minutes or so, you come across a well-placed oversized bench which provides an excellent view point of the south-western end of Nant Gwynant, and of the ancient hill-fort of Dinas Emrys.

Although the tree cover makes it hard to see the detail, Dinas Emrys is an extension of the rhyolite that we saw earlier. It is surrounded on all but its eastern end by steep rocky slopes, but is connected to the east by a narrow ridge. This is one of a handful of sites in Wales from which early medieval artefacts have been found and is connected with the legends of King Arthur (though whether there is any real connection is open to speculation as there is no convincing evidence either that Arthur really did exist, although it does seem likely that he did, or of the region of his origin).

Carry on down the track until at about 6006 4926 where there is a yellow and red signpost. Turn left here, down to a large gate. Go through the gate, head right towards Craflwyn Hall and then down the drive to a gate onto the road.

Alternatively, instead of turning left at the first red sign, you can extend the walk westwards, for another 850 metres or so, by following the red and then green signpost arrows. The signposted trails are not marked on the OS map, but are easy to follow and a leaflet showing them is available from the National Trust. Inquiries about access to Dinas

Nant Gwynant

Emrys should be made to the National Trust warden's office situated near the car park at Craflwyn.

On reaching the main road, either use the Sherpa bus (infrequent) to return to the start, or turn left and walk east for about 250 metres, cross the road and turn right (signposted 'Sygun Copper Mine'), and cross the bridge. A visit to the mine is highly recommended and includes a trip underground (allow at least one hour).

Immediately after crossing the bridge, turn left onto the footpath and follow to Llyn Dinas (850 metres); the crags on the right as you approach the lake are LRT. Follow footpath on the right-hand side of the lake, eventually leading you to Llyndy Isaf Farm, then on meeting the minor road (at about 6275 5022) turn left, and then right at the main road, and follow road (300 metres) back to the to car park and bus stop.

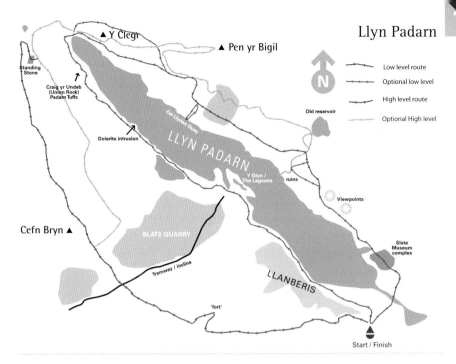

▲ Y Clegr
▲ Pen yr Bigil

Standing Stone

Craig yr Undeb (Union Rock) Padarn Tuffs

Dolerite intrusion

Cei Llydan Quay

LLYN PADARN

Old reservoir

Y Glyn / The Lagoons   ruins

Viewpoints

Cefn Bryn ▲

SLATE QUARRY

Slate Museum complex

Tramway / Incline

LLANBERIS

'fort'

Start / Finish

N

— • — Low level route
— • — Optional low level
— • — High level route
——— Optional High level

Walk #10 – Llyn Padarn

Llyn Padarn is a classic glacial valley lake – long, narrow and very beautiful indeed, despite the industrial remains that litter either side. Actually it is now only a shadow of its former self. After the ice in the valley had all melted there was one long lake, encompassing both Llyn Padarn and Llyn Peris. Some of the land south-east of Llyn Peris at its head would also have been part of the lake, as was the land that now separates the two lakes and also the low, flat land that extends for almost two kilometres beyond Llyn Padarn's north-western end. The two lakes combined are currently about 5 kilometres long, with the land that was once part of them the total stretch of the original lake would have been about 8 kilometres long.

Indeed after prolonged heavy rain (not unusual in the area) the flat area beyond Llyn Padarn is often flooded and, from high up on Moel Eilio or the north-western flanks of Elidir Fawr, you get an idea of what it must have looked like a few thousand years ago.

Llyn Padarn

The two lakes have long been the focus of habitation in the area and, in more recent times, of industrial activity. Whilst the walks around the lake concentrate on the physical geography, it is impossible not to take notice of present and past habitation and industrial activities.

Two alternative walks are offered here. An easy and relatively short low level and a much more gruelling high level walk. Both walks would be suitable for a day when the higher hills are enveloped by the clouds and views are restricted. However, both walks unite at the north-western end of the lake where there is a classic view of the Llanberis Pass and the summit of Snowdon behind the lake from the bridge, made all the more enthralling if the hills are visible and especially if the day is windless and they are reflected on the lake surface. On such days you will enjoy one of the best views in Wales and in Britain.

Low Level

START	▶	LLANBERIS BUS INTERCHANGE, MAES PADARN (5822 5990)
FINISH	●	CIRCULAR ROUTE
TIME	⟳	3 HOURS
GRADE	⊙	NAVIGATION ●
	⟳	TERRAIN ●
	⊗	SEVERITY ●

This is the easiest of the all the walks, especially on the Llanberis side of the lake where it uses an old railway line. There, however, is some height that has to be gained on the Parc Padarn side of the lake and some short steepish sections towards the end of the walk in the woods. The route around the glacial lake takes you through areas of the Llanberis Slates and the Padarn Tuffs, with plenty of outcrops of both to be seen.

The walk passes through several wooded areas with restricted views, but there are plenty of spots where the views are truly superb, including the classic viewpoint at the northern end of the lake (halfway through the walk).

From the start point, enter Maes Padarn fields and head towards the lake, keeping the buildings close to your left, crossing a stile. As you get close to the lake, bear sharp left and follow the lake's edge. The route doesn't need to be described in detail as it is only necessary to keep as close to the lake as possible, so I have only pointed to places of special interest. However, when you reach the paved path, with large blocks of stone on either side (below a car park), do turn round for a great view of the Llanberis Pass and Dolbadarn Castle.

The path soon ends and you are diverted for a couple of hundred metres onto the pavement. Turn right at the first junction, again using the pavement until the first gap in the stone wall on your right; turn right through the gap and head towards the lake edge.

This area, properly knows as Y Glyn, is popularly known as 'the lagoons' and is built up from slate waste from quarries on the hillside and dumped into the lake. This is a popular picnicking spot and a training place for budding canoeists and there are plenty of paths to choose from as well as seats to rest upon. At the end of the lagoons, pick up the old railway track alongside the lake edge, shortly passing under an elegant cast iron footbridge.

A little further on the track runs on a causeway with an isolated part of the lake on your left. Shortly after this lagoon ends, you should notice a wooden bench on the right-hand side of the track and directly opposite it a yellow-topped wooden waymarker post on the left. Carry on until the fourth waymarker post, starting with this post as number one. Around the fourth post there are some steep crags on your left and a small rise in the ground on the right. Almost directly opposite the waymaker post, you should notice a narrow track going over the small rise and then dropping down to a rock outcrop at the lake side. This is at grid reference 5637 6170.

This is a good spot to enjoy views of the lake. The rock outcrop is a dolerite intrusion and is somewhat tougher than adjoining rocks, thus it sticks out slightly into the lake. Return to the old railway track and continue for another 100 metres or so, up to the entrance to a tunnel. Just before the tunnel you should see on the right another small track which ascends up to the road. Go up this track and turn right onto the pavement.

Carry on along the pavement to a footpath/cycle track on the right (actually the old road) and follow it. After a couple of hundred metres you come to a large outcrop of the Padarn Tuffs. This is known as Craig yr Undeb (Union Rock) as the North Wales Quarrymen's Union was founded here (when one landowner turned a blind eye and allowed the site to be used for meetings). The outcrops of the tuffs are well worth studying for the detail of the rocks and also provide some enjoyable opportunities for scrambling up and over them, if so desired.

Llyn Padarn

Photo w10.1 | View from north-west end of Llyn Padarn. The great ice sheet 'outlet' and 'valley' glaciers of the ice age extended beyond this point having carved down into the bedrock to create the basin now filled by the lake.

Carry on to the end of the lake and cross the bridge with, at the eastern end, classic views of the lake and the mountains beyond. On those rare occasions when the wind is absent, the reflections of the mountains in the lakes intensify the quality of the view (see photo w10.1).

Here there is a choice. For a direct route, bear right after the bridge and follow the road for the next 1.5km up to the footpath sign on the right (at about 5757 6178) – directions continue below when the alternative route arrives at this footpath sign.

A much more interesting option (but one for which you'll need the OS 1:25,000 OL17 map) is to bear left at the end of the bridge and continue to a signposted footpath (actually a dirt track with nameplate Tai Felin) at about 5589 6261; bear right and follow the dirt track which soon swings sharply right and reveals a terrace of houses on the left and a view opens up of an enclosed bowl with outcrops of the Padarn Tuffs all around. This shaping of the land, with alternate flat-bottomed, boggy bowls and sharply rising outcrops of tuffs will be repeated over and again as you follow the footpath to rejoin the main route later on.

Follow the track to beyond the terrace of houses and just before the entrance to a farm named Tyn Tyll. The footpath turns left passing through an old iron gate (at 5615 6261) and rises up past an outcrop of the tuffs. The track then swings right and left. Follow the track with a stone wall on your left for about 125 metres, until you join another dirt track (at about 5632 6270). Here you turn right and follow the footpath (ignoring a stile on the left), and carry on through the yard of a smallholding, after which you enter an area with plenty of ruins of abandoned cottages. This is a view on what life was like in the area just 50 or more years ago.

There are in fact plenty of tracks (the access routes for the old cottages) in addition to the public footpath and it really doesn't matter if you follow one or the other. The objective is to reach the point where the two marked footpaths converge at 5678 6227 and a gate into Parc Padarn about 25 metres further on.

This section of the footpath takes you up over Y Clegyr, but in a dip between outcrops, thus denying you views. However, look out for a gap in the vegetation on the left near the top, just as the track starts to descend, where you can easily gain access to the top of an outcrop of the tuffs for fine views over the lake and mountains. Return to the footpath and continue down to the road at about 5698 6197, turn left and follow the road up to the footpath sign at about 5757 6178.

Both routes: Turn to the right, off the road and down an initially steep track which soon joins a dirt track. Follow the dirt track. There is a café (with limited opening hours) after about 100 metres and a path with steps down to Cei Llydan at the lakeside, where there are seats for picnics (however, it is necessary to re-ascend to the dirt track to continue).

A short distance further along the dirt track, a bridge crosses above the track – this is an old quarry tramway route used to transport slate waste for tipping. Further on you cross a deep trench in the rock, another exit from the slate quarry. The quarry itself can be seen just beyond here through a gap in the rocks on the left – where you can peer cautiously into the old workings.

Continue along the dirt track until it ends at the boundary with Parc Padarn, just after you cross a stream (on a bridge of large slate slabs), with a cascade of small waterfalls rising off to the left. Immediately after entering the Parc there is an option (turn sharp right) of a visit down to the vegetation-covered ruins of an old woollen mill (later a writing-slate manufactory). Or to continue the walk, take the left fork up through the woods. After gaining about 50 metres on a rocky path you come to a small clearing on a nose of rock with superb views to Snowdon and the hills behind Llanberis. The rock here is a dolerite intrusion and accounts for the prominence on which you are standing. On either side of dolerite, the rocks are the softer slates and you now begin to descend. After another 150 metres or so there is a wooden bench and more excellent views.

Another couple of hundred metres brings you to the old quarry hospital, now open as part of the National Slate Museum. Turn right down the wooden steps in front of the hospital to a viewing point on an old slate tip (now covered with grass) for fine views back along the lake. Follow the track around and down, and then turn sharp right to cross a bowed bridge. The track then leads you towards the museum and its various attractions – this part of the track can be flooded after heavy rain, but there are several other tracks to choose from. For details of the museum see 'Quarry walk', Walk 13.

To return to the start, follow the road alongside of the museum, turning right at its end, cross the footbridge and follow the track (to the right of the railway) back to Maes Padarn.

The walk can be extended to encompass Llyn Peris if desired – from the museum ascend one of the paths (see museum map boards and/or leaflets) to the viewing point (mentioned in chapter 2) at 5910 6040, then follow the footpath through the quarry to 5997 5962, then descend the wide zigzag footpath to the southern end of Llyn Peris and return to the start on the pavement alongside the road on the lake's south-western side (add 1.5 hours).

High Level

START	▶	START OF FFORDD CAPEL COCH ROAD (5783 6010)	
FINISH	●	CIRCULAR ROUTE	
TIME	⟳	5 HOURS	
GRADE	⊙	NAVIGATION ● ●	
	☁	TERRAIN ● ● ● ● ●	
	❸	SEVERITY ● ●	(NEVER FAR FROM ROAD)

While the low level walk around the lake is pretty easy, this alternative route is extremely tough going. It is fairly easy in terms of macro-navigation, but crosses some very rough terrain with twisty, easy to lose tracks – and in some places, on the first half, with no track at all. The horribly tough terrain – with hidden holes lurking beneath each clump grass or heather – makes for extremely hard going and means that I cannot overemphasize the point that this is a walk for experienced hillwalkers only. However, the route offers consistently excellent views in all directions and is a real moorland walk on the higher level section on the western side and the first half of the eastern side.

Photo w10.2 | Alexandra Quarry, centre left, seen from Bwlch y Groes.

From the main road, follow the minor road uphill, turning right opposite the impressively large chapel (Capel Goch – red chapel), then left (at 5753 6010) and follow tarmac track uphill to 5671 5949 where the tarmac track turns right and gives way to a dirt track. After 200 metres, go through a gate (5664 5967). Here a short diversion to the right, alongside an old stone wall, is recommended to the summit of a small iron-age 'hill-fort' atop an outcrop of the Bronllwyd Grits (at 5670 5983) with very fine views of the lake and surrounds.

Return to the dirt track and follow it up, through a first gate, carry on to just over the top of Blwch y Groes and a second gate at 5567 5993 (ignore a stile crossing a stone wall, seen on the right just before the gate comes into view). From here you have a great view to the west to the Alexandra Quarry across the Gwyrfai valley. The quarry workings have cut right through the hill-top, leaving a gap looking like a badly decayed tooth stump. The knobbly shape seen on the low summit of the hill to the right of the quarry is a volcanic breccia.

Turn right immediately after the gate and follow the track; after about 75 metres (5566 6002) you should notice an old iron gate in the stone wall on the right (not accessible as it is behind a modern barbed wire fence). Beyond the gate a track curves away to the left (its route marked by the remains of old slate fence posts) towards what looks like the two stranded gable ends of a small house on the skyline. Looking in the other direction, to the left, you can see a slight ditch, actually an old track, which runs from the gate towards the quarries on the western side of the hill.

Llyn Padarn

Photo w10.3 | The summit of Cefn Du with heather in bloom – the white rocks are rhyolitic Padarn Tuffs.

The track in the ditch is the old bed of a tramway used to carry slate from the quarries on the western side the hill to the old ruin, which is actually the remains of a winding house at the top of an incline used to lower slate to the railway line next to Llyn Padarn.

Carry on towards the summit, along one of several tracks. At one point you pass between quarries (behind safety fences) to both the left and right. Only about 100 metres separates the two quarries and shows how close Cefn Du became to being hacked right through, as happened with the Alexandra Quarry.

You then pass out of the slates and soon into the Padarn Tuffs; there are a few small outcrops of the Padarn Tuffs on and around the route to the summit and beyond – mainly welded tuffs, but with some easy to spot breccias near the summit (see photo w10.2).

You will notice some ruined buildings at and near the summit, and spread all around there are plenty of old concrete blocks. These are all part of the remains of an old Marconi transatlantic wireless transmitter from the 1920s. The main building still exists lower down the hill (at about 5350 6120) and is now an outdoor pursuits centre. The concrete blocks are where the transmitter mast guy lines were anchored into the ground.

It is worth pointing out some other nearby aspects of early telecommunications as a contrast to the general run of industrial archaeology of the uplands.

There's the Holyhead-Liverpool 'visual' telegraph (a sort of 'semaphore' system) which was one of the world's first such networks (and the first to be set up and operated by commercial interests and not by the state military apparatus). It was used to transmit advance information to the markets in Liverpool of the arrival of a shipload of cotton or whatever from across the Atlantic. Ships arriving off Holyhead would signal details of their cargo to a telegraph station at Holyhead, the message then being relayed by a series of stations all along the coast (including three on Anglesey and one on Ormes Head, Llandudno) to Liverpool, where dealers would re-adjust prices in advance of the arrival of the ship. Though they now seem rather quaint, it was the visual telegraph that ushered in the modern era of global telecommunications with the ubiquitous mobile phone and broadband internet access.

On either side of present day Bwlch Maesgwm, you can spot the remains of pairs of old telegraph poles and in places piles of old insulators. At one spot the stumps of a pair of posts have been converted into a bench overlooking Llyn Cwellyn and the Gwyrfai valley. On older maps Bwlch Maesgwm is marked as 'Telegraph Col' and the poles are the remains of an old transatlantic telegraph cable which passed this way. So around here (if we include Anglesey as 'around here') you can find the remains of three generations of early telecommunications technologies – the early nineteenth century visual telegraph, the early twentieth century electric telegraph and the early twentieth-century transatlantic wireless – as well as old farms and quarries. In the early twenty-first century (in 2005) broadband lines came to Llanberis, plugging it into the modern global telecommunications network and allowing anyone, anywhere, to look at webcams of the mountains or to track weather data from hillside sensors.

From the summit, there is a choice of routes. The slightly easier and shorter option is to return to the point where the quarries have narrowed the hilltop to just over 100 metres wide. Bear left at 5520 6023, picking up the line of a footpath (marked on the OS map) to a gate and a slate stile at about 5533 6026; follow the public footpath (noting the immense quarry workings to your right) to 5543 6043, where the footpath splits into two. Follow the left-hand route, heading at first roughly north-west, then just west of north to a ruined stone wall. You then have to aim for a stile at about 5488 6162 (the track is easy to lose and anyway disappears after the ruined stone wall is crossed, if not before, and later on you need to cross some very wet ground to get to the stile – pick the best route you can between the higher ground represented on the OS map by 'spot height 289' and the two ring contours at around 5490 6145). The terrain is dire, with innumerable hidden dips between the rough vegetation and will test your patience. From the stile head to the Standing Stone at about 5470 6183 (note that the stone is located on the ground just above the 'g' of 'Standing' on the OS map).

Llyn Padarn

For the slightly longer and significantly rougher route, continue along the summit plateau aiming for the Padarn Tuff outcrops at around 5410 6134 (Garreg Lefain). A track helps initially, but bears off left and you must at some point or other strike out across trackless and extremely awkward heathery or grassy terrain again with innumerable dips and holes at every step. From Garreg Lefain head due north towards the Stone Circle marked on the OS map at about 5405 6170 (more extremely hard, trackless going I'm afraid), then pick up the track marked on the OS map at about 5410 6162 (the footpath shown on the map does not exist on the ground). Follow track heading just south of east, passing near several Hut Circles and Burnt Mounds (these mounds are probably late medieval/early Tudor in origin and are generally thought to have been used to farm rabbits), then head to a stile at about 5452 6165 and then to the Standing Stone (see end of previous paragraph).

The Standing Stone, the Stone Circle and Hut Circles probably date from pre-historic times and demonstrate that this was a well-used area a few thousand years ago. From the Standing Stone head eastwards alongside the stone wall to pick up the footpath at about 5482 6182 and follow path to the minor road at about 5484 6206, turn left and follow the road for 50 metres to Lon Bwlch (shown as a footpath on the map) and descend to the village of Cwm y Glo; follow lane/path all the way to main road and cross (with very great care) to opposite side, turn right along pavement for 150 metres, then left just after Y Fricsan pub and hostel. Almost immediately turn right behind garden centre along old road (closed to traffic) and follow it to the lake (crossing another main road).

Turn left across the bridge and the classic views at its eastern end, turn right on the minor road along the lake's north-eastern shore for about 500 metres (passing the dog leg at the end of the lake railway after about 250 metres). Ignore gaps in the wall on the left until you see a 'Parc Padarn' sign with a red 'Tân/Fire' sign underneath it (and opposite it, on the other side of the road, a parking place). Here turn left up an obvious track which ascends through woodland to the base of an outcrop of the Padarn Tuffs, frequently used by trainee climbers. Go east past the base of the cliff where the climbers learn their art, and either scramble steeply up the gully to the left, or half-walk, half-scramble up the much less steep crags beyond the gully, up to the ridge and continue to the 'summit' at 5655 6230. Alternatively scramble up the steep rock face on the northern side of the outcrop (experienced scramblers only as the last part is quite steep).

Enjoy the views and then prepare to set out for the most difficult part of the walk. From the summit, the track is easy to pick up initially, but it soon proves to be very hard to follow. There is a track all the way, but it twists and turns dramatically, often appearing to disappear, but look hard enough and you will find it somewhere in the dense mass of waist deep heather

Photo w10.4 | Pen yr Bigil; Snowdon in the distance on the right.

and gorse (shorts, or indeed trousers made with thin material, are definitely not advisable!) One point to keep in mind is that the track often makes its way via the numerous outcrops of the Padarn Tuffs – so if it appears to disappear, try the nearest outcrop and see if you can pick up the track again the other side of the outcrop. It takes an apparent eternity to cover just 400 metres to meet the footpath shown on the OS map that crosses north-west to south-east across Y Clegyr – and be warned, the footpath is not visible at all until you stumble across it so despair is probably inevitable at some stage on this 'walk'.

All this may sound awful (and it is!), but the views (and the variety of colour from the vegetation) make up for all the difficulties. Hard work indeed, but definitely worth the effort

On meeting the footpath a choice can be made whether to resort to the road (by turning right onto the footpath, then left along the road) or to struggle on up to Pen Y Bigil (see photo w10.4). The going is even harder for the first 200 metres or so, but after that it is much easier. The track is very hard to find initially, but goes around the right (southern) side of the first prominence after the footpath, but leads you, if you can find it, to easier grassy terrain and an easy ascent to the summit and more superb views.

It is all too easy to head south from the summit to meet the road at about 5758 6173, but this takes you off access land, so it is properly necessary to return to the footpath at 5696 6202, turn left and left onto the road. Follow the road to the second footpath sign (at the end of the coniferous wood) at about 5765 6175 and follow that footpath (this is

Llyn Padarn

about 100 metres further on than the first footpath sign, which is the route followed in the low-level option).

It would be difficult to give precise details on this path as it twists and turns quite a lot, but it is generally (with reference to the OS map) easy to follow the right route (which passes a couple of spots which are densely vegetated by stinging nettles in summer – another reason not to wear shorts on this route!) Watch out for the section starting at 5783 6159 and continuing downhill for about 30 metres to an old metal gate. There is an unguarded quarry on the right here – but it is all but impossible to see due to dense tree cover, so don't go off to the right as there are big drops. The quarry is best seen from just past the metal gate when it is safe to go carefully off to the right, but don't get too close to the edge.

After more twists and turns you will eventually arrive at Cae Goronwy (at 5809 6144) where the path differs from the route shown on the OS map as it is diverted around the back of the farm, taking you to a farm track (at 5818 6147). Turn right and follow the track downhill to the entrance gate to Parc Padarn about 100 metres further on.

Stop on the bridge shortly further on. Looking downhill, you can see that the stream cuts through a 4 metre high embankment. This was a dam enclosing a reservoir in the flat area behind you. The hillside below the embankment was intensely quarried (though much of the evidence for this is now hidden by vegetation) and the reservoir was used to power machinery in the writing-slate manufactory (now vegetation-covered ruins) at the bottom of the hillside (originally it was a woollen mill).

Carry on along the track to the end of the dam and turn right, heading down the signed footpath. It's difficult to see but there is plenty of evidence on the rock faces of quarrying as you descend the path. Half-way down the track crosses a wooden bridge over the stream – this is a delightful spot when the stream is in spate with a cascade of waterfalls above and below you (but watch out for the slippery wood when wet). The track carries on down the hillside and passes a deep quarry gash on the left some way down. Join the dirt track and turn left back across the stream and into Parc Padarn (for the third time). For further details see the last four paragraphs of the low level walk.

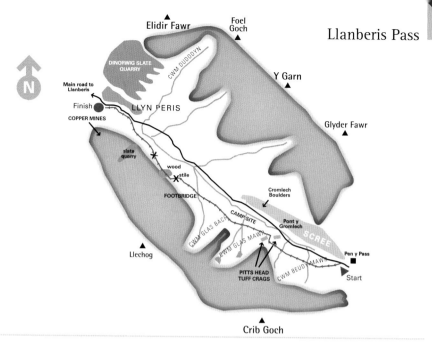

Walk #11 Llanberis Pass

START   ▶   LLANBERIS BUS INTERCHANGE (5822 5990)

FINISH   ●   CIRCULAR ROUTE

TIME   ☻   3½ HOURS PLUS

GRADE   ◐   NAVIGATION ●

           ☁   TERRAIN   ● ●

           ✖   SEVERITY   ●

The Llanberis Pass, between Pen y Pass and Llyn Padarn, is one of the scenic master-pieces of central Snowdonia.

It was carved deep into the mountains by ice flowing out of the Migneint ice sheet as an 'outlet' glacier, breaching the pre-glacial watershed. This glacial action took place partly along the line of the some of the most massive eruptions of the Snowdon Volcanic Cycle, eruptions which led to the collapse of the Snowdon caldera. The area between Gyrn Las (separating Cwm Glas Bach and Cwm Glas Mawr) and Pen y Pass marks the north-eastern boundary of that caldera. This walk takes you through the centre of the volcanic and glacial action which created this marvellous landscape.

The entire length of the Pass can be walked 'off road' except for the final section alongside Llyn Peris which requires use of a pavement. The views down the pass are outstanding and remain so for the entire length of the walk.

It takes about three hours each way to walk between Pen y Pass and Llanberis, although there are plenty of opportunities to cut the walk short (for example, at the parking place near the Gromlech boulders or at the Nant Peris car park). There are also plentiful spots which repay a short diversion along the way, thus adding to the time needed. So this can be either a half-day walk or can easily be extended into a full day if you go off to explore rocks or valleys on the way down.

I describe a one-way walk from Pen y Pass to Llanberis, thus going downhill most of the way. There is a wealth of geological features to be seen, including some amazing rocks and over powering glacial features. An array of 'hanging valleys' and resulting waterfalls is strung along the length of the pass on either side. The cliff faces left exposed by the glacier also provide plenty of opportunity to study various types of rock. From Pen y Pass to beyond northern end of Cwm Glas Bach you pass through various volcanic rocks. From there to Llanberis the rocks are mainly sedimentary, but with a number of intrusive igneous rocks cutting across the valley forming distinct prominences or ribs.

On the south-west (Snowdon) side of the pass there is access land for most of the way to Llanberis, but on the other (Glyderau) side access land ceases to reach the valley floor northwards from south of Nant Peris.

Navigation should not be a problem as the main job is to head down the valley, keeping first the road, then later the river, on your right and the base of crags on your left. However, there is no specific path, often not even a whiff of a track on the ground in many places, and it is not necessary to follow a set route; in many sections you can choose whether to follow a higher or a lower line, or to meander back and forth as you see fit. There is no need to follow the particular route I describe, except if you want to see the particular rock examples mentioned.

However, there are a few points (stiles, gaps in walls, bridges) that need to be reached at specific places. I have identified these by grid reference.

Photo w11.1 |
View down the
Llanberis Pass,
a glacial trench
carved out of the
tough volcanic rock
by powerful ice
sheet 'outlet' and
'valley' glaciers
at the height of
the ice age.

From the start of the walk the views along the pass, towards Llyn Peris and Llyn Padarn, are entrancingly beautiful. Very soon after leaving the start point the mountains start to rear upwards on either side providing a dramatic frame for the rest of the walk all the way to Llanberis. This is a great walk on a cloudy day as the mist only rarely reaches lower than 350 metres, so usually there are good views down the valley even if they are impeded when looking upwards.

Start along the Pig Track until, shortly after leaving the car park, you pass a low stone wall. Break off the track to the right, heading underneath the power lines and down the valley. As you go, keep close to crags, rather than staying close to the power lines and the road.

For the first kilometre or so, all the crags off to the left and the right are Lower Rhyolitic Tuffs, the main Snowdon volcanic rocks — mainly around here are air-fall tuffs with few distinguishing features, but you can see the occasional outcrop of breccias. After passing the second stream, the crags to the left start to change to dolerite. These dark dolerite rocks are easy to see in the crags behind a bowl where a stream falls out of Cwm Beudy Mawr. A cottage ruin near 6351 5594 makes a good point to stop and look around and up at the cliffs rearing up all around.

A stone bridge crosses a stream at 6341 5598. The bridge looks decidedly slippery and tilts alarmingly downwards, but despite its looks it is not slippery even in the wet, though it obviously requires care when crossing. A gate in a stone wall follows immediately after the bridge and a narrow track then guides you down and along, past a tiny trial quarry and on to another stone wall. Cross the wall at the low point and continue along the track, which leads to a stile (made difficult by sets of cross-bars at the top). Cross and keep roughly to the crest of the ridge.

When you reach a run-down stone wall, look up to the approaching cliff face on the left, Dinas Mot. If you look closely you should be able to see the junction between the lighter LRT at the bottom of the cliff, and the darker dolerite behind and above it.

Carry on to the end of the crest of higher ground, stepping over a wire fence a few metres before the edge of some crags. Here the view of the lower reaches of the pass and its twin lakes is superb. There is plenty of space to sit and view the scenery from here. The crags below you are popular with trainee climbers and you may have someone suddenly appearing in front of you. More experienced climbers use the bigger and much more frightening cliffs on either side of the valley – you may hear their shouts to one another or see them clinging to improbably steep slabs of rock (the light coloured LRT rocks referred to above make up one favourite climbing face).

The rock on which you are sitting is the Pitts Head Tuff, the first of the Snowdon volcanic rocks. We will have a closer look at the rock when we carry on, but for the moment enjoy the view of the lower pass, the crags above you on both sides – and don't forget to turn around and look back up the pass to Pen y Pass. Over the other side of the pass you can see the crags of the LRT running down from Pen y Pass, followed by a sharp, asymmetric ridge made up of basalt lava.

To continue, re-cross the fence and head to the left of the crags towards a stone wall that passes in front of the crags and leads you to another dodgy stile. Cross the stile carefully and drop down to the bottom of the crags (see photo 3.1). This is still the Pitts Head Tuff, but first, if time and inclination allow, I recommend a diversion here to the other side of the road, so drop down to the road and bridge. Cross the bridge, clamber up the stone wall on the other side and head towards some massive blocks of rock about 150 metres further north along the road (one of the blocks juts out onto the road).

These are the famous Cromlech boulders, much favoured by 'boulderers'. Our interest in them is that they display some superb breccias, with lumps as large as television sets in places. It is well worth walking round the various blocks to see the different faces of the LRT breccias (see photo 4.2).

Return to the bridge – spending a bit of time on the way looking at some of the smaller blocks above the massive boulders on the way back – here you can see a vast variety of LRT rocks, some clearly bedded, some displaying cleavage (and some showing both bedding and cleavage) and plenty of good examples of breccias (see photo w11.3). You can also explore some of the other fallen blocks beyond the bridge too if you have time. There are some excel-

Photo w11.2 | The south-western flank of Glyder Fawr, mainly Lower Rhyolitic Tuffs, later carved through by an ice sheet 'outlet' glacier that breached the pre-glacial watershed at Pen y Pass to create the glacial Llanberis Pass.

Photo w11.3 | Breccia in Lower Rhyolitic Tuff, near Pont y Gromlech (on the north-eastern side of the valley).

lent examples of siliceous nodules in the Pitts Head Tuffs among the blocks to the north-east of the bridge.

After crossing the bridge, head back up following the base of the PHT outcrop for about 150 metres, looking at the variety of rock types within the PHT, mainly welded tuff, but also rocks with siliceous nodules (see photos 3.3 and 3.2). At the far end of the outcrop, leave the PHT outcrop and head towards the base of the scree and some massive blocks of rock which have fallen down from the cliff face.

As you approach these blocks, look up to the cliffs (Dinas Mot, which you looked at earlier and saw the lighter coloured LRT below and the darker dolerite above). Here you can see again the difference between the two rock types. The LRT produces cleaner, bigger slabs than the dolerite and is preferred by climbers.

The boundary of the top of the LRT with the dolerite is easy to spot here, but so is the LRT's lower boundary. It can be seen at the bottom of the slabs of LRT just before the scree, where the slabs give way to 'columnar jointing'.

Head now towards the next stone wall and a stile adjacent to the bottom of the scree. After crossing the stile, keep well to the left, heading uphill towards a prominence. At about 6300 5638 you should see a ruin, unusually a double structure (marked on the OS map as 'house platform' indicating a medieval origin). Carry on to the top of the prominence, a product of intrusive rhyolite. Rhyolite dominates the walk for the next 1.5km or so, intruded into the LRT rocks when they were still hot. All around here you are walking around some of the main fissure-vents of the LRT eruptions. The centre of the eruptions was all around here, especially in the cliffs of Gyrn Las high on the left forming the north-western edge of Cwm Glas Mawr. The emplacement pattern left by the molten magma as it was intruded is visible in the shorn off rock face high up on Gyrn Las, to the right of a waterfall coming out of Cwm Uchaf. You could explore the lower reaches of Cwm Glas Mawr from here if you want to, by heading left, picking a path through boulders to the bowl behind spot height 396 (at about 619 563). If you are tempted further up into Cwm Uchaf or Cwm Glas remember that you will also have to get back down. There are two practicable routes, either left of the stream from Llyn Bach or to the right of the stream running down a rocky slope that drains the area to the east of Llyn Glas. It is highly inadvisable to go up into any of these cwms, Cwm Glas Mawr, Cwm Uchaf or Cwm Glas, if there is mist about – or indeed any chance that they may become misty. A mistake when selecting the route of descent could be fatal as there are precipitous crags all around.

To continue the main walk, head down towards the Climbers' Club building at Ynys Etws and a gate at 6234 5680, pass through gate and then a gap in a wall (entering the Blaen y

Nant campsite), bear left and head to another gap in a wall. Aim then for a stile next to the stream (to leave the campsite). From here look up into Cwm Glas Mawr, surely one of the most forbidding views in Snowdonia. From the dark, dank cliffs of Dinas Mot on the left, straight ahead to the threshold of the lower cwm and glimpses to the distant upper cwms, and to the looming cliffs of Y Gyrn on the right, this is where volcanic rock can be seen at its thickest and where glacial action has cut through that tough volcanic rock to its deepest extent.

Cross the wooden bridge and head slightly uphill, half-left on an obvious track. As the track passes a ruin on the left, the views down the valley open out. A short distance in front of you is a massive 'erratic', a block of rock that has fallen from above and been transported a short distance before being dumped by ice.

Take advantage of the viewpoint here to scout the next stage of the route. In the middle distance you can see how the land rises from the river in a series of crags. First the crags rise from the river in two hump shapes, then there is a wide flat area before another set of crags. The route aims for the base of that set of crags.

Photo w11.4

Flow-banding in intrusive rhyolite, Llanberis Pass (height of rock, approximately 3 metres).

Llanberis Pass

To get there, continue up the obvious track to another Climbers' Club building. Keep an eye on the boulders to the left, where there are some fine examples of 'flow-banding' in these large lumps of intrusive rhyolite. Pass in front of the building and two trees. Pick up a clear but narrow track that rises a little then levels out and wends a way through vegetation and low, stop/start stone walls and eventually past a ruin (on the left). The track heads towards the base of the crags identified earlier on, and as it approaches them crosses a minor stream on two slabs of rock taking you directly towards an obvious gap in the stone wall, but don't go through it, instead bear half-right past the second of two slanting rocks, then bear left and cross the stone wall (with built in steps on the other side) to follow a stone path to the base of the crags.

It doesn't matter if you don't follow this precise route – you can go along the river if you prefer, or follow a route higher up above the minor crags. The footbridge mentioned below is the next 'collecting' point (and is only necessary anyway in flood). However, if you do follow this route, as you approach the crags you will see some extremely impressive flow-banding in intrusive rhyolite (6173 5711) – see photo w11.4 and for a close-up of the same rocks see photo 4.8). Carry on past the next set of crags and more flow-banding, until you come close to a stone wall (bracken can obscure the track for 25 metres or so on either side of the stone wall). Head for a low point in the wall and with useful steps built into the wall (on this side, but not the other), then aim for the base of the next set of crags, still intrusive rhyolite, but here redder in colour (6160 5720).

Carry on, swinging to the left round the end of the crags, with Llechog coming into view high up on the ridge line (see photo w11.5). Aim towards a low stone wall and a ruin beyond it (near some ice-smoothed flat rocks). As you approach the ruin the view opens up left into Cwm Glas Bach and the stream coming down from it with some fine waterfalls. At about 6134 5724 a bridge crosses the stream, but is only essential in wet weather. Again you can explore up into Cwm Glas Bach if you wish. There are some impressive waterfalls higher up and way up there is even a small glacial cwm, Cwm Hetiau, probably only active towards the end of the ice age when this was one of the few places where ice could collect and gather despite the increasing temperature. Hetiau means 'hats' and the cwm is so named because travellers in the open carriages of the early Snowdon Mountain Railway trains often had their hats blown off by the wind when the train passed above this cwm on the exposed ridge line. The route up into the cwm is fairly clear, but again do not venture up here if there is mist or any prospect of mist descending as it would be very easy to stray onto potentially dangerous ground.

From near the bridge look up into Cwm Glas Bach. Here we are roughly at the northern corner of the Snowdon caldera. The great Idwal-Hebog fault zone and syncline run through

Photo w11.5 | Llechog on the Llanberis Ridge – formed from intrusive rhyolite and outcrops of the Lower Rhyolitic Tuffs. Note the syncline showing through the outcrops in the upper reaches of Cwm Glas Bach (upper left), a continuation of the Cwm Idwal-Moel Hebog syncline.

Cwm Glas Bach. Indeed the continuation of the syncline, so well seen in Cwm Idwal, can also be seen, though less clearly, at the top of Cwm Glas Bach, in the V-shaped rock outcrops near the ridgeline.

Llechog is made up of intrusive rhyolite, LRT and PHT. Outcrops of the three volcanic rock types come down the mountainside to meet your route. The PHT, however, is hard to spot as you cross it inside a wood a bit further on.

From the footbridge, scout the next section of the route – once across the stream you want to aim below the next set of crags, then aim back upwards to the diagonal erratic you can see on the next nose beyond the crags. Just beyond this erratic you can see a fence. An essential collecting point is a stile (at 6113 5739) hidden behind the diagonal rock.

Cross the stile and follow a track contouring to and then through the wood. The exit stile (at 6102 5753) is hidden behind a large erratic at the far side of the wood. Cross the stile (you can see some good examples of the welded tuffs of the PHT on fallen blocks around here) and then head half-left onto the ridge of high ground. On reaching the ridge you should see crags ahead with a low stone wall in front (not the large stone wall farther up the hill on the left). Head towards the front of the crags. On crossing a small stream you should see a gap in the wall, leading to the front of the crags, follow round, using a groove in the rocks (basalt lava).

This is another good spot to sit and soak up the views. Head round the crags, swinging left and down over some rocks to a complex of sheepfolds (the rocks can be slippery when wet). Look at the rocks behind the first sheepfold. These are the crags you have just come around, the basalt lava, and about two metres above the base you can see some amazing shapes in the rocks above the sheepfold.

Cross the boggy area and stream, aiming for a stone wall and a ruin. Follow the stone wall, keeping it just on your right, for 250 metres to a stile (6063 5766). Follow the track across a bracken field (where the chest-high bracken can make it difficult to see the path and can soak you after rain) to the river and onto a footbridge at 6037 5825. For Nant Peris, cross the bridge and follow the footpath to Nant Peris. Or, to get to Llanberis, keep on along the valley heading towards Llanberis along a footpath.

You pass varieties of Ordovician and Cambrian sedimentary rocks on the left as you walk towards Llanberis. The slate quarry you pass on the left is in Ordovician rock. Immediately after the quarry there is a small sandstone quarry. From near where you meet the road you may be able to spot the waste tips of copper mines on the left above the crags. Follow the road, with clear views of the extent of the workings at Dinorwig Quarry on the other side of the lake, to a footpath leading to Dolbadarn Castle which is worth a diversion, or carry on along the road directly to Llanberis.

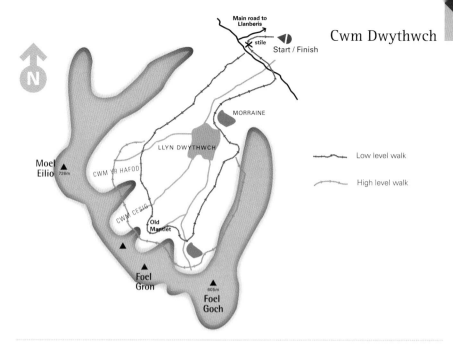

Walk #12 Cwm Dwythwch

This surprisingly impressive walk takes in the four immature glacial cwms in the upper reaches of Cwm Dwythwch, below Moel Eilio and the surrounding area. The cwms developed at a late stage in the Ice Age after the melting of the main glacier in the lower Cwm (present site of the lake). Each of the four cwms held a small glacier all of which combined to produce a single glacier in the main cwm. This glacier built the moraine that hides Llyn Dwythwch from view until you enter the lower cwm itself. The four small high level cwms are all sited on geological weaknesses such as rock junctions, faults and/or synclines.

The walk provides outstanding views of lower Snowdon, the northern Glyderau and Llyn Padarn as well as different aspects of Cwm Dwythwch. What is most unexpected is the sheer size of these immature cwms from within. From a distance, as well as from immediately below and above, they seem to be insignificantly small hollows that lack interest. However, from within their scale is substantial.

Cwm yr Hafod and 'Old Mantlet' are especially surprising. Cwm yr Hafod sits in the upper corner of a much bigger bowl, providing a 'balcony' viewpoint of Cwm Dwythwch. Old Mantlet also needs to be seen from within; no real idea of the size of the cwm can be gained from above or below it.

The mountain rearing above you also generates a feeling of incorporation into this landscape, rather than just walking on it. The walk ends with a visit to the strip of land between the lake and its moraine. This too is a surprisingly large landscape. The feeling of remoteness here is intense, despite the proximity of Llanberis.

There are two suggested routes. One follows an awkward track (where a track exists) linking the cwms at around 450 to 500 metres, however in the second half of the walk the track crosses very steep grass slopes and is at the limits of practicability. Some may find the steepness of the slope daunting, so the second option tackles the cwm at lower level and provides a fairly easy walk (the only drawback being that it is a bit boggy in places). There are several fences in the cwm and the routes take account of the crossing points – except that, at the time of writing, one barbed wire fence that has to be climbed on the higher level walk as the stile has been taken away, and one on the lower level version where the stile has fallen over.

High Level Route

START	▶	LLANBERIS BUS INTERCHANGE (5822 5990)
FINISH	●	CIRCULAR ROUTE
TIME	🕐	4 HOURS PLUS
GRADE	●	NAVIGATION ●
	●	TERRAIN ● ● ● ●
	●	SEVERITY ● ● ● ●

This is a tough mountain walk even though it reaches only 500 metres in altitude, taking you into remote areas with superb views. It is demanding, crossing steep grassy slopes with crags below. It is inadvisable to do this route when the grass is wet as a slip would have potentially serious consequences. However, if you do tackle the route you will gain an intimate view of

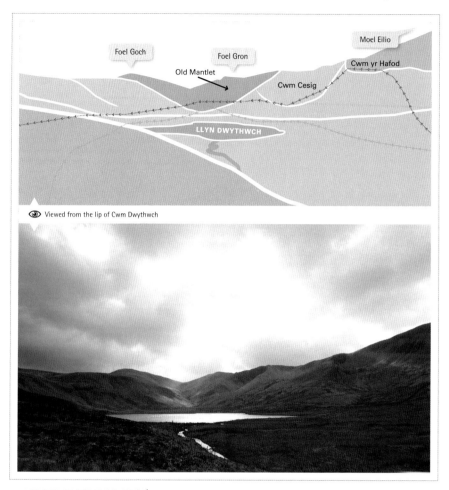

Viewed from the lip of Cwm Dwythwch

Diagram w12.1 + Photo 12.1 | Cwm Dwythwch and Llyn Dwythwch and its
four immature glacial cwms: Cwm yr Hafod, upper right; Cwm Cesig, centre
right; 'Old Mantlet', centre; Unnamed glacial cwm, centre left.

these immature glacial cwms and a good understanding of what a glacial cwm would look
like in its early stages of development.

Start from the bus interchange point, near Snowdon Mountain Railway, and head up
Victoria Terrace, turning right just before the end of the road, then 200 metres on turning left
and using footpaths (passing Ceunant Mawr waterfall viewing point) to reach the farm house
near a road/farm track junction at 5727 5916. Turn left and immediately cross stile 5728 5905;

Cwm Dwythwch

follow track, after 150 metres crossing a stream aiming to pick up the track (shown on the OS map) at about 5700 5865 and follow it roughly south-southwest into the cwm.

The steep slope to the ridge (Moel Eilio's north-eastern ridge and the northern arm of the cwm) is made up of the Carnedd y Filiast Grit (Cambrian sedimentary rock, which also forms summit of Elidir Fawr in the Glyderau). However the top of the ridge itself is made of the later and softer Ordovician mudstones and siltstones. The soft rocks were partially metamorphosed by heat from a nearby intrusion of igneous 'microgranite' (forming present day Mynydd Mawr). This toughened the rocks and as a result the 'soft' siltstones here form the mountain summit. This is an example of a 'metamorphic aureole'.

A little further along the track, Llyn Dwythwch comes into view. Often windswept and bleak, the lake feels intensely remote (see photo w12.1 and diagram w12.1). At about 5665 5805 where three stone walls converge, the route options diverge.

Go through gap in wall, bear right following stone wall to 5630 5787. Here you turn right into a sheepfold on the other side of the wall, immediately turning left and passing through the shelter to come out on the right-hand side of the stone wall (and south of the wire fence that runs up the hillside from here). Pick a route up the steep grass hillside, aiming for the right of Cwm yr Hafod (5700 5760), then slog upwards.

Cwm yr Hafod, the summer cwm, forms a small bowl, at about 490 to 500 metres, within the greater bowl of Moel Eilio. The floor of the cwm is boggy, but towards the back is a complex of sheepfolds and a stone wall – no doubt part of the cwm's summer role in earlier days. It's a good place to sit and appreciate the views below and to study the cwm itself. You are very unlikely to meet other people here, though you may see some in the distance on the ridge.

The headwall is asymmetric, with the summit of Moel Eilio forming the highest point. The low point in the headwall, directly behind the cwm, (Bwlch Gwyn) is on a major weakness. It is a fault line; it is also the junction between the Carnedd y Filiast Grits and the Nant-Ffrancon beds, and it stands on the line of an anticline formed during the mountain building episode about 400 million years ago. This combination of factors provided the weak point that allowed Cwm yr Hafod to be developed by accumulation of snow and ice in a gully or cleft, then widening to bowl shape.

The track leaves the cwm a few metres above the sheepfolds, at about 500 metres, traversing round, above crags initially then over steep grass slopes, into Cwm Cesig (5620 5715). Drop 50 metres into bowl of cwm, which is wide and shallow, the least impressive of the four cwms, but also the biggest. Unlike Cwm yr Hafod, there is little to delay over here. Traverse round to a wire fence, cross and search out for very narrow track at about 450 metres that traverses directly into the next cwm, 'Old Mantlet' (5630 5680). This traverse is where the first steep, potentially hazardous section starts as the slope is just about crossable, but only just, and is best avoided in wet weather when it may be slippery. If in doubt, at the expense of needing to regain some height, you can drop down next to the fence until the slope eases and then move across and climb back up into 'Old Mantlet'.

'Old Mantlet' is well worth the visit, for it is a much bigger cwm than you expect from below, surprisingly so, with an enclosing arm and steep rock walls rising all around creating a remote, isolated feel. There are several sheer gullies in the rock walls, the weak points where the small glacier dug back into the rock.

'Old Mantlet' itself is presumably the sharp gully in the upper western corner of the cwm that is such a noticeable feature when walking along the ridge top, but here it is really fairly insignificant, unless you scrabble up towards it for a closer look. Similarly, when looking down from the ridge top, the cwm itself is pretty insignificant looking, just as it is from below; and it is only from within that you begin to get a feel for the actual scale of this immature glacial cwm.

The next stage of the high level traverse crosses above some steep crags and is potentially lethal. If you want to avoid this section, drop down 100 metres to below the lowest crags, pick up the stream coming out of the last cwm, and climb up beside it to the highest bowl. Otherwise pick up the faint track from the cwm that traverses the bluff or nose of rock on steeply sloping grass above the crags until the slope eases then descend a nose into the last cwm.

The unnamed cwm is in many respects the least cwm-like of the lot, hardly distinguishable from a steep, narrow valley, except for the wide shallow area forming the cwm floor (5670 5660); indeed it is insufficient as a feature to earn a name on the OS map. Like Cwm Cesig, this cwm has been developed below a low point in the ridge, the steep-sided col between Foel Gron and Foel Goch, which is aligned on a fault. The cwm began to develop in a gully formed below the col. There is an impressive moraine perched high up in the cwm, around 5680 5660 (see photo w12.2 and diagram w12.2).

The best point for gaining an overview is above this bowl where a track on the left takes you to just below the col.

From the cwm pick up the track that heads north-east onto the side of the ridge, Cefn Drum (the same track as that which rose up to the viewpoint described above, so if you went there, you have to retrace your steps or pick up a yet higher track from the col itself). Eventually this will lead you onto the flat ridge, where you will encounter a new barbed wire fence. The stile on the old fence has been removed and not (yet?) replaced on the new one. There is a stile on the summit of Foel Goch which is the only option if you don't want to climb

Cwm Dwythwch

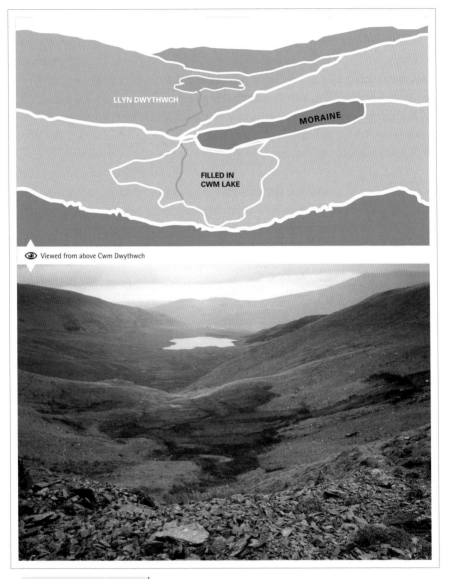

Diagram w12.2 + Photo 12.2 | Cwm Dwythwch from above the unnamed glacial cwm; the low ridge centre right is a moraine.

the barbed wire fence. The alternative to the summit is to carry on, keeping the fence on your right until where it suddenly veers left and descends steeply to the lake. Cross carefully at the corner using the bracing pole and hope that those responsible return the missing stile.

After crossing the fence, bear right and pick up another, older fence and follow till a section where the barbed wire is missing and cross there. If you miss this point, just follow this fence down and round to and through a gate to a nearby stile at about 5739 5755.

After crossing the old fence, head down to cross a stream near rock outcrops, then aim for the stile at about 5739 5755, cross and turn left. Follow the narrow track all the way along the eastern edge of Cefn Drum till a wider track is met, turn left and follow it down through a stone wall, then bear left and head towards the lake. The strip of land between the lake and the moraine is a good spot to sit and take in the glacial scenery through which you have walked.

Follow the stream down to the farm track and turn left up to farmhouse and follow the footpath back to the start.

Low level route

START	▶	LLANBERIS BUS INTERCHANGE (5822 5990)
FINISH	●	CIRCULAR ROUTE
TIME	☾	3 HOURS
GRADE	☝	NAVIGATION ●
	☁	TERRAIN ● ●
	☯	SEVERITY ● ●

This route is an excellent walk on a day when the clouds are low down and leave few other opportunities for hillwalking. The walk takes you round Cwm Dwythwch at a level where the sheer unexpected size of the cwm is omnipresent. The four small glacial cwms higher up the slopes are easily seen and from this angle quite impressive. Indeed, they are at their most impressive when the cloud cuts off their higher reaches, then the cwms look even larger than they do when it is clear. I've included an option to climb up into 'Old Mantlet', one of the four cwms which is probably the most interesting from within and is well worth a visit.

The start is the same as for the high level walk up to when you come to a three-way junction of stone walls at 5665 5806, head to a stile and gate at 5655 5749. The views up into

Cwm Dwythwch

Cwm yr Hafod and Cwm Cesig are excellent. Then cross a very boggy section to another stile at 5658 5732. At the time of writing this stile is lying on the ground, but there is a section of fence without barbed wire which can be stepped across fairly easily at this location.

From here I recommend climbing up into the cwm marked 'Old Mantlet' on the map, by working your way up and across towards the outlet stream and then following it up into the inner cwm. It is the most atmospheric of the four cwms and surprisingly large, providing a quiet, remote viewpoint (see comments about the cwm in the high level walk description). Then I'm afraid it's a steep drop back down again and around to the next cwm and a small waterfall at its base.

If you don't go up into 'Old Mantlet', continue around towards the waterfall at the base of the fourth cwm.

Again there's the option here of going up into the cwm and following the higher level track, or continuing round at lower level. For the former see above. For the latter, cross the stream and pick a course near the base of the crags (cleaved siltstones in the Nant Ffrancon formation) on the right until the crags fall back and a bowl opens up with several ruined sheepfolds. Continue round the headland at the base of the crags to a stile at 5708 5747. Around here you cross from the Ordovician Nant Ffrancon formation siltstones into the Cambrian Carnedd y Filiast Grits (no cleavage) and over the next couple of hundred metres (crossing a stream on the way) you see some interesting outcrops in the crags on the right, including some exposed bedding planes, some showing ripples left by waves when they were first laid down (see photo 1.11). These exposed outcrops are part of an anticline but this is very hard indeed to see.

The next point to aim for is a stile at 5715 5775 in a stone wall (which can be seen descending from the hillside after the exposed beds). From here follow the track towards the head of the lake then bear left to the strip of land between the lake and its retaining moraine, another good spot to sit and appreciate the remoteness of the cwm. Follow the stream (very boggy in places) back to the farm track (at about 5758 5871). Turn left to reach farmhouse and footpath back to start.

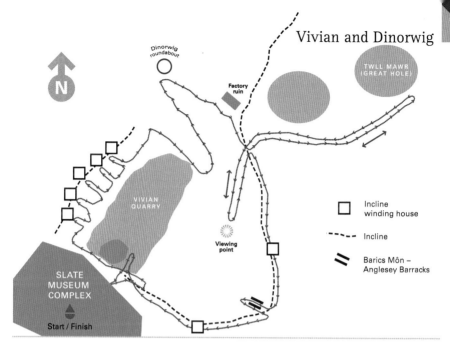

Vivian and Dinorwig

- TWLL MAWR (GREAT HOLE)
- Dinorwig roundabout
- Factory ruin
- VIVIAN QUARRY
- Viewing point
- SLATE MUSEUM COMPLEX
- Start / Finish

☐ Incline winding house

---- Incline

≡ Barics Môn – Anglesey Barracks

N

Walk #13
Vivian and Dinorwig Quarries

START	▶	WELSH NATIONAL SLATE MUSEUM, GILFACH DU (586 604)	
FINISH	●	CIRCULAR ROUTE	
TIME	☕	4–5 HOURS PLUS	
GRADE	☉	NAVIGATION ●	
	☁	TERRAIN ●●	(STEEP STEPS)
	⚡	SEVERITY ●	

The ruins of old quarries dominate Llanberis and have defined its history, culture and architecture. The remains are a reminder of the role of mountain areas in the industrial revolution and are well worth walking around for gaining a small insight into what they may have looked like in their active days. They are also, of course, of great interest geologically. The quarry cliff faces reveal information about bedding, cleavage, folding, faulting, igneous intrusions and intervening strata of sedimentary sandstones.

Significant parts of the old quarries on either side of Llanberis are fenced off, although the fences are widely ignored by local climbers, walkers and courting couples. There are two reasons for staying out of the fenced off areas. First, it is trespass. Second, there is a real risk of injury or death from falling rocks (either from quarry faces or waste tips) or collapsing ground. That said, some of the public footpaths are extremely dangerous and subject to rock falls; also one footpath shown on the OS map in the Glyn Rhonwy Quarry area leads to a dangerous and narrow gap between two deep quarry pits, with a collapsed fence ready to trip you up. So, just as much care is needed at all times, even on public rights of way.

Two quarry areas slightly further afield are not fenced off and can easily be walked through and without need to trespass (but not of course without danger from rock or tip falls). These are the Alexandra Quarry (start at Betws Garmon, following footpath through caravan site from 5358 5757) and the Dorothea Quarries (start at Nantlle, footpath from 5095 5338). If visiting the Alexandra Quarry make sure to include a trip to the summit tor of Moel Tryfan – a fascinating volcanic breccia (and, very regrettably, a prime example of modern municipal vandalism with an 'interpretation' board screwed into the summit rock face).

A booklet currently available from tourist offices and the National Slate Museum describes several walks through old quarrying areas, takes you round some less conspicuous relics of the slate industry.

I have outlined a fairly short walk around the old quarry workings on the north-eastern side of Llyn Padarn using public footpaths and paths mostly within Parc Padarn.

This walk takes you through two old quarries, one comparatively small and the other relatively large. The Vivian Quarry is itself a lot larger than many smaller quarries that were once in operation, but is overshadowed by the gigantic Dinorwig Quarry. Once these would have been bustling noisy places, but today they are quiet, visited only by walkers and feral goats.

The starting point for this walk is the National Slate Museum at Gilfach Du, part of the Parc Padarn country park on the north-western side of the lake. A trip round the museum provides an excellent introduction to slate quarrying and working, with film clips showing

Photo w13.1 | Vivian Quarry.

the old quarries at work, a massive water-wheel, lots of artefacts from the narrow-gauge railways used in the quarries and extensive metal-working workshops. Admission to the museum is free. Leaflets outlining different walks around Parc Padarn and the quarries are available at the museum.

After touring the museum, head towards the Vivian Quarry, go through a narrow tunnel entrance (after crossing the railway), to the quarry and its flooded pit, nowadays much used by divers (see photo w13.1). From here a quarry can be seen from inside – note the sandstone outcrop on the left interleaved with slate and which the quarry workers have left standing, also note the overhead cable carrying slate. The transportation of slate – either to waste tips or to the railhead for shipment to ports on the Menai Straits or Caernarfon – was a major factor in the quarry operations, as evidenced by the effort that obviously went into building the inclines and overhead cables that can be seen around here.

You can also see how the quarrying was performed at different levels, with the quarry slowly becoming bigger and cutting further back into the hill.

Leave the Vivian Quarry and immediately outside the entrance, turn left up the lowest section of an incline with rails still in place. Leave the incline using a gap in the wall on the left a short way up. Join a tarmac track, turning left and crossing to the other side of the track for views over the Vivian Quarry and its flooded pit. Carry on to a signposted track on

Photo w13.2

Vivian Quarry.

the right, made out of slate steps, and follow it up to the next level, then head left past old 'gwaliau' ('shelters' where the slate was split) to the winding house at the top of the restored section of the Vivian Quarry incline where you can see slate-filled trolleys. Above you can see the incline rising further up the hillside. Return to the signposted track and continue up to further levels, exploring each level if desired as far as the incline and then returning and ascending yet again. You can see how the slate would have been moved out of the quarry at

Photo w13.3 | Cwm Dwythwch and Llyn Dwythwch from Dinorwig Quarry.

each level and along to the incline. It's a stiff climb up the slate steps, but eventually the climb comes to an end and you meet a track across a wooden stile.

At the top admire the profusion of that most modern of invasive species – interpretation boards and health and safety notices. Cross the stile and turn right and follow the path around the top of Vivian Quarry. Ignore minor paths off to the left, also try to ignore a veritable forest of waymarker signposts and more notice boards (one of which kindly imparts the opinion that 'people could be seen as a form of invasive species'); also ignore a track off to the right and carry on round to join a dirt track at 5892 6060; bear left and follow the track uphill through a small terrace of houses and on to the roundabout at Dinorwig (marked as parking place on the OS map at 5905 6108).

All the ground to your left and much of it to the right is 'remade' land, with filled in quarry workings and tips. Old photographs show that this whole area was once a mass of old workings. If you look carefully you can distinguish the remade ground from the yellowish grass that has been planted (and is shown as purely white areas on the OS map with no contour lines). Despite this restorative work, the area is still dominated by the massive waste tips that rise up to the right and ahead.

Bear right at the roundabout and follow the signposted footpath (shown on the OS map) round towards the viewing point (mentioned in chapter 2). As you come round the view opens up progressively to the massive workings and waste tips. At the south-eastern end of a large workshop you get views of the top sections of a very large incline that brought the waste down to the lake and the railway. Visit the viewing point for superb views of the quarry and the surrounding mountain- and lake-scape (see photo w13.3). The quarry is often at its most impressive (and its most depressive) when the clouds prevent you seeing the top of the workings and the quarry looks as if it might go on upward forever.

Return to the base of the incline, and go through the left-hand swing gate; follow the footpath further through the quarry to just beyond the highest point on the path, noting the very large pits to the left and the massive size of some of the fallen blocks of rock all around. This takes you through some 'jaws' of rock on either side – here again you can see the sandstone which separates workable beds of slate. After peering into 'Matilda' (the massive hole on the left just after the highest point and marked on the OS map) turn round and return to the pair of swing gates and descend the path on the lower section of the incline.

Follow down the incline, passing through a winding house, and start to descend a second leg. Two-thirds of the way down this second leg of the incline, you come across a row of buildings on the right. This is the Barics Môn (Anglesey Barracks) where quarry workers from Anglesey stayed five nights a week.

Bear right and walk down the centre of the two rows of barracks and come out onto a track, turn left and follow the track downhill. Shortly you come out onto a metal bridge, crossing a slate tramway level below. The winding house to the right is the one you could see earlier on immediately after leaving the Vivian Quarry. You can descend on this incline back to the museum (steps to the left just before the metal bridge take you to the tramway level) or carry on over the bridge and follow the walled footpath as it zigzags down initially through slate waste tips, and later on through the woods, bringing you out at 5872 6004 between Llyn Peris and Llyn Padarn.

Acknowledgements

Thanks go in particular to Dr Peter Hodges, Clair Drew, Phill George, Lisa George, Reg Atherton, Ian Smith, Michael Evans, Emma Williams, Paul Davis and Debbie Neale who all read parts of the draft and provided useful comments on my early efforts. Reg Atherton also acted as 'guinea pig' for several of the recommended walks. Discussions with Dr Tim Matschak on the subject of science writing have also been very helpful. My thanks go to Professor John Cole and Dr Peter Hodges of the National Museum of Wales, to Dr Norman Moles and Professor Rory Mortimore of the University of Brighton and to Roger Cordiner of CCE Sussex University, for help in identifying the 'Cruziana' fossil (photo 2.14) I came across while researching the geology of the area. Thanks to the Geological Society of London, Reg Atherton and Ian Smith for permission to use photographs, and to the staff of the British Geological Survey for arranging permission to reproduce several items from BGS publications. Also thanks to Franco Ferrero and Peter Wood of Pesda Press for enthusiastically supporting the project. My thanks to Phill George, Bryn Williams, Pete Gallimore and the staff of Camre Cymru/Outlook Expeditions, Llanberis, for excellent mountain leader training and Katherine Wills of Active First Aid, Llanberis, for equally excellent outdoor first aid training. Robert Dudley kindly very kindly provided help in my search for a publisher for which I am grateful. A book of this nature depends very heavily on the scientific writing and research work of many people. I have listed the books and other works consulted below, but special mention must be made of M Howells et al., Ordovician (Caradoc) marginal basin volcanism in Snowdonia north-west Wales, published by the British Geological Survey (unfortunately at a price which means that the reader can only conceive of accessing it through a library or academic institution) which was the key text for the details of the Snowdon Volcanic cycle; Kenneth Addison and his series of pamphlets on the ice age in central Snowdonia, played a similar role for the chapters on glaciation; Bryan Lynas's book, Rocky Rambles in Snowdonia, inspired me to dig further into the fascinating geological history of Snowdonia.

Photo copyright: All photos by the author except: photo 6.1 John Simmons, The Geological Society of London; photo 6.5 and photo 6.12 by Reg Atherton; and photo 6.7 and photo 6.9 by Ian Smith.

British Geological Survey: Map 0.1, Diagram 1.3, Map 2.2, Diagram 3.1, Diagram 4.2, Diagram 4.3, Diagram 5.4 and Map 6.1. Sketch maps in this book are reproduced based on the 1953 Ordnance Survey map sheet 107 ©Crown Copyright.

Pattern swatches based on Public Review Draft Digital Cartographic Standard for Geologic Map Symbolization (PostScript Implementation) by the U.S. Geological Survey (Open File Report 99-430).

Books and pamphlets consulted in writing this book:

K Addison, Classic Glacial Landforms of Snowdonia, 1997.

K Addison, Snowdon in the Ice Age, 1988.

K Addison, The Ice Age in Cwm Idwal, 1989.

K Addison, The Ice Age in Y Glyderau and Nant Ffrancon, 1989.

D Bick, The Old Copper Mines of Snowdonia, 2003.

J Bollard (transl), The Mabinogi, 2006.

D Browne & S Hughes (eds), The Archeology of the Welsh Uplands, 2003.

P Crew & C Musson, Snowdonia from the Air: Patterns in the Landscape, 1996.

J Davies, A History of Wales, 1993.

A H Dodd, The Industrial Revolution in North Wales, 1971.

N Edwards, Landscape and Settlement in Medieval Wales, 1997.

J Giles (transl), Nennius, Historia Brittonum (History of the Britons).

D Gwyn, Gwynedd: Inheriting a Revolution: The Archaeology of Industrialisation in North West Wales, 2006.

M Howells et al., Capel Curig and Betws-y-Coed, 1978.

M Howells et al., Snowdonia, 1981.

M Howells et al., Dolgarrog, 1981.

M Howells et al., Geology of the Country around Bangor, 1985.

M Howells et al., Ordovician (Caradoc) Marginal Basin Volcanism in Snowdonia North West Wales, 1991.

M Howells & M Smith, Geology of the Country around Snowdon, 1997.

A Hunter & G Easterbrook, The Geological History of the British Isles, 2004.

I A Jones, Enwau Eryri: Place-names in Snowdonia, 1998.

G Jones and T Jones (transls), The Mabinogion, 1993.

D Kirk, Snowdonia: A Historical Anthology, 1994.

C Lees & G Overing, A Place to Believe In: Locating Medieval Landscapes, 2006.

B Lynas, Snowdonia Rocky Rambles: Geology Beneath your Feet, 1996.

F Lynch, A Guide to Ancient and Historic Wales: Gwynedd, 1995.

F Lynch, S Aldhouse-Green, J Davies, Prehistoric Wales, 2000.

F North, Mining for Metals in Wales, 1962.

G Dyfnallt Owen, Elizabethan Wales: The Social Scene, 1964.

A Richards, Slate Quarrying in Wales, 1995.

P Rhind & D Evans (eds), Plant Life in Snowdonia, 2001.

B Roberts, The Geology of Snowdonia and Llyn: An Outline and Field Guide, 1979.

D Williams, The Cistercians in Wales, Vol 2, 1983.

D Williams, Atlas of Cistercian Lands in Wales, 1990.

N Woodcock & R Strachan (eds), Geological History of Britain and Ireland, 2000.

Glossary of Geological & Geomorphological Terms

Breccia – volcanic rock containing visible lumps of rock.

Caldera – roughly circular-shaped depression caused by volcanic explosion

Continental crust – a section of the earth's outer surface, the crust, that forms a land mass. The edge of a continental crust usually extends some distance out to sea, with a continental shelf. About 25% of continental crust is below current sea level as the boundary with oceanic crusts is fairly deep undersea. Continental crusts are less dense and more buoyant than oceanic crusts, but also thicker – the average thickness of continental crusts is about 35km and can be up to 75km thick where new mountain ranges are being built (such as the Himalayas). The crust rests on top of the earth's outer mantle forming the 'lithosphere' which is split into 'tectonic plates'.**Erosion** – the physical breakdown of rock by water and ice. The rate of weathering and erosion is often related to climate (low temperatures lead to glaciation, hot ones to desertification, for example, each with their own patterns of erosion and weathering), but the relationship is complex and controversial.

Fault – a crack in the earth's surface, ranging from quite small to very large, where rocks move in relation to one another. Faults also provide routes to the surface for molten magma lying under the surface.

Fault line – the surface expression of a fault; also giving terms such as fault-line scarp and fault-line lake.

Geomorphology – the scientific study of the form of the land surface and the processes which affect it at the interface between the lithosphere, the atmosphere, the hydrosphere and the biosphere. So, while geology is largely concerned with the creation of the underlying rocks, geomorphology concentrates on the forces that shaped the rocks into the landscape.

Glacier ice – the dense 'blue ice' of which glaciers are made up has an air content of less than 20%; firn contains 20-30% air, 'granular ice' (a pre-firn stage of ice development) 30-85%, and snow 85-90%. As snow accumulates over the years, due to its not melting during cold summers, the snow particles lower down are compressed and deformed, subject even to some partial melting and refreezing into ice made up of smaller particles. These particles coalesce to form firn. Continued snow accumulation leads to further compression and the creation of solid and dense glacial ice.

Graben – traditionally a rift or rift valley (graben is German for trench), where the land drops down between two roughly parallel faults; but now grabens are also recognised as occurring in much less regular form, not as straight lines, but curved and asymmetric, with multiple linear and cross faults. A half-graben is an area of land that drops down on one side only. The volcanic activity in central Snowdonia took place around fault zones which formed a graben.

Igneous or volcanic activity – falls into two main types: first, 'extrusive' where magma erupts at the surface as molten lava or explosive 'pyroclastic' fragments; and second, 'intrusive' where the magma doesn't reach the surface but is intruded between layers of soft rock below the surface (and may be later exposed at the surface by erosion).

Igneous rock – see 'Rock types'

Ignimbrite – rock produced by highly explosive and extremely hot pyroclastic eruption; also known as 'welded tuff'.

Isostatic rebound – during glaciation, the weight of the ice compresses the crust and upper mantle. After the ice has melted the land surface rebounds. The same effect occurs, but on a much longer timescale, as rocks are eroded and weathered away.

Lithosphere – the earth's crust and the upper part of the mantle (lithosphere means the 'sphere of rocks'). The lithosphere is divided into a set of interlocking 'tectonic plates'.

Magma – molten (or partially molten) rock from the mantle, which accumulates in reservoirs under the crust when melting is caused by factors such as subducting oceanic plates. Magmas are chemically very complex and change depends on conditions; indeed they undergo change from the time of production to that of eruption. Magma contains gases as well as elements. For example, gases are released as a result of chemical processes and are held in bubbles within the magma under pressure, waiting to escape as if opening a bottle of 'fizzy' water. Though often only present in small quantities gases can have an important effect on the type of eruption if the gases cannot escape. Rhyolitic magmas tend to be quite viscous and this has the effect of retarding the escape of gases within the magma. As the magma rises up towards the earth's surface, pressure falls and more gases are released as water, carbon dioxide and other gases are formed in the liquid magma, forming more and more bubbles and/or increasing the size of existing bubbles. The viscous magma acts to retard the growth of the bubbles, increasing pressure within them. When it becomes too high compared with that of the encasing liquid magma, the magma is transformed from a liquid holding bubbles to a gas holding molten fragments (pyroclasts) of bubbly liquid (a process known as 'exsolution') which then creates the highly explosive eruptions of gas and fragments common with rhyolitic magma. Magma reservoirs may produce both rhyolitic and basaltic eruptions from the same magma source.

Oceanic crust – Basaltic lava erupting at the surface, along with lower-lying intruded basaltic rocks (including 'gabbro'), form new oceanic crust which spreads outwards from the zone of eruptions (the 'mid-ocean ridge'), to be recycled by subduction, where the oceanic crust collides with the rocks of other oceanic or continental crusts. Oceanic crusts are generally relatively young rocks (up to about 200 million years old at the margins) and are much thinner than continental crusts, but also denser.

Metamorphic rocks – see '**Rock types**'

Orogeny – the process of building mountain ranges caused by the collision of two continental plates. The plates buckle, crack and fold, building upwards to create mountains.

Nueé Ardente – the type of eruption which produces welded tuffs and ignimbrites.

Oceanic crust – section of the earth's outer surface, the crust, underlying an ocean.

Outcrop – strictly speaking the bedrock or rock nearest the surface, but which may be covered by 'superficial' deposits (unconsolidated peat, alluvium and so on). However, I have used it to mean what it says, 'rock that crops out' visibly on the surface and through any superficial deposits. Geologists also use the term 'exposure' for this.

Plate tectonics – the theory that the earth's surface is formed of independent but interlocking plates which are driven in circulation by convection currents within the underlying mantle (though there is no agreement on whether this is the sole, or even the major, cause). There are about a dozen major plates and several smaller ones, each moving independently of the others, sometimes into collision with each other. Plates can carry oceanic crust, continental crust or both. The plate boundaries are the site of most (but not all) volcanic activity (and also of earthquakes). It is currently believed that the continents join up into a supercontinent and then break up into continents cyclically over periods of about 500 million years. Events such as the opening and closing of the Iapetus Ocean and subsequent collision of Avalonia and Laurentia were events in such a cycle. At the time of these events the area was not in its present position, but was south of the equator, and has over the last 400 million years floated on the convection currents to the present locations. There were more minor earth movements too – the Lake District is further away from Snowdonia today than it was in Ordovician times (due to movement along major north-east to south-west trending fault zones). Another point worth noting is that collision is more likely to be oblique than fully direct. Plate movements are not all the same – the most rapidly moving plate, the Pacific oceanic plate, is currently moving at about 10cm per year, whereas the African continental plate is static.

Pyroclast – any fragment expelled in a volcanic eruption – as opposed to flow of molten lava – though the fragments can contain lumps of molten magma. The fragments can be very small (known as 'ash') to extremely large (several metres in size) and can be solid, liquid or gaseous (or a mix) at the time of eruption.

Rhyolite/rhyolitic – rhyolites or rhyolitic rocks are the most common form of igneous rocks in North Wales. This is comparatively rare as most volcanic eruptions produce basaltic or intermediate (andesitic) rocks. Rhyolitic rocks have less iron and magnesium than basaltic rocks and more silica and potassium (rhyolitic rocks have over 66% silica; intermediate rocks between 52 and 66%; and basic rocks less than 52%). This is believed to happen because iron and magnesium have a higher melting point than other elements, especially silica and potassium. So, when the mantle rocks start to melt, a rock of rhyolitic composition can be produced at lower temperatures than those of basaltic composition – if the molten portion can be separated from the original mass of rock. This is thought to explain why, in Central Snowdonia for example, a lot of the erupted rocks from the Snowdon Volcanic Cycle are produced first as rhyolitic material, followed by basaltic eruptions. Rhyolite and rhyolitic are essentially synonyms, but do have different uses – rhyolitic is applied to any 'acid' or rhyolitic rocks (rhyolitic lava, rhyolitic tuffs etc), whereas rhyolite is a name given to intrusive rhyolitic rocks. Rhyolitic rocks are more viscous, so flow less easily and cool down in vents, leading to subsequent build up of gases and underlying molten magma, resulting in highly explosive eruptions.

Rock types – rocks are usually divided into three great types: igneous (or volcanic), sedimentary and metamorphic. All rocks start as igneous material, erupted or intruded by one means or another to form rock. Igneous rocks are very complex with over 1,500 different classifications, often overlapping and contradictory. Essentially igneous rocks can be 'acid' (i.e. rhyolitic or granitic), intermediate (andesitic) or 'basic' (basaltic or doleritic). Oceanic crust is made up of basaltic rocks, while continental crust is usually made of andesitic or intermediate rocks (named after the Andes where they occur frequently). Rhyolitic rocks are comparatively rare, but predominate in central Snowdonia because of the phase of plate collision and subduction. Roughly, acid rocks are light-coloured (due to high proportion of light-coloured felsic minerals and are quartz and feldspar rich), while basic rocks are generally darker (due to being iron and magnesium rich). Currently, about 4 million cubic km of extrusive igneous rock and between 22 and 29.5 million cubic km of intrusive igneous rock are produced annually across the globe (from about 25 to 35 million cubic km of magma). The rocks produced by igneous activity can then be eroded and weathered into smaller pieces which are carried away, usually by water or ice, and deposited, eventually forming sedimentary rock (which can also be formed by sediments of biogenic, biochemical and organic origin, such as limestone, and sedimentation of other materials, such as 'evaporites'). 'Detrital' grains are held in a much finer-grained 'matrix' and cemented by minerals that develop as a result of chemical processes. The processes of erosion, sedimentation and transformation into rock ('lithification') can be repeated several times. Nearly all the naturally occurring minerals can be rock grains, but the distribution is limited because some minerals and rock types are more stable, quartz being the most stable and thus the most common grain in 'sandstones'. Mudrocks are the most common of sedimentary rocks and are a mixture of 'clay' (grains less than 4 microns in size) and 'silt' (grains of between 4 and 62 microns). Igneous and sedimentary rocks can also be subject to high temperatures and/or pressures by later tectonic activity, and which can cause changes to the minerals within a rock type, transforming it into a different type. Two important effects of metamorphosis are noted in sedimentary rocks in central Snowdonia – the transformation by pressure generated by mountain-building activity of mudstone into slate, and the hardening of the rocks forming peaks such as Moel Eilio and Foel Goch (Glyderau) by heating caused by intrusion of hot igneous rocks (forming a 'metamorphic aureole' in the surrounding rocks).

Tectonic plate – Strictly speaking tectonic plates consist of the crust (either or both continental and oceanic) and the upper mantle (the lithosphere), however for ease of comprehension I have referred in the text to 'continental plate' and 'oceanic plate'.

Tuff – unfortunately the term 'tuff' suffers badly from being used very inconsistently by geologists, so I have simplified its use. Strictly speaking a tuff is the rock produced from volcanic ash. And a volcanic ash is any pyroclastic fragment less than 2mm in size (it is not ash in the everyday sense of the term, the residue of combustion). Fragments between 2 and 64mm in size are called 'lapilli' and the hardened rock with such fragments is known as 'lapillistone'. Rock with fragments in excess of 64mm in size is 'breccia'. However, in recent years the intermediate lapilli/lapillistone terms have fallen out of fashion and most geologists now only distinguish between tuffs and breccias, but without updating the strict definitions. I have adopted this practice and only refer to tuffs and breccias, using a rough and ready means to distinguish between the two – i.e. any pyroclastic or intrusive rock with easily visible lumps is a breccia and any with fragments too small to be seen by simple oversight with the naked eye is a tuff. There are many types of tuff (and breccias too). There are 'air-fall tuffs', 'ash-flow tuffs' and 'ash-surge tuffs' and so on. Also a tuff can have a small mixture of lump sizes and still be a tuff or tuffite depending on the proportion of lapilli or non-igneous matter to be included in the mix). More confusion is added when welded tuffs are included, for they contain fragments ('lapilli'), usually of pumice, that have been flattened and welded into the smaller fragments, and this regardless of the size of the pumice fragments. To add yet further confusion, tuff is used for 'formation' names – the Lower Rhyolitic Tuffs (which include tuffs, whatever, if anything, geologists today call lapillistone, breccias, siliceous nodule rocks, contemporaneously-intruded-rhyolites, and so on). So the reader will no doubt forgive me for having simplified the use of tuff to mean all these things without great distinction, i.e. rock formed out of igneous fragments (pyroclasts) and identifying breccia in this sense as a sub-form of tuff. Purists may object, but in actual fact this is how the term is often used by geologists, despite the traditional formal definition. The definition I have used comes from the book Volcanoes by M Rosi and others (2003), 'deposited pyroclastic rock that has consolidated'. This does not include a definition of the size of the fragments, so I apply it to where the fragments cannot be easily distinguished by the human eye in rock outcrops.

Welsh Words

'Snowdon' is the English name for 'Yr Wyddfa' and both names can be applied to the summit and to the whole massif (which stretches north to beyond Llanberis). 'Snowdonia' is the English name for the Welsh 'Eryri' and has usually meant the mountainous areas around the Snowdon massif, but there is no real agreement on exactly how far that area covers. The bureaucratic boundaries of the Snowdonia National Park Authority stretch south to include the Rhinogs and Cader Idris. For the purposes of this book, I have restricted coverage to 'central Snowdonia', i.e. the Snowdon massif and the Glyderau, adding a short section on the Carneddau. This restricted area has a coherent geological/geomorphological history, has had a lot of work done on it by geologists, and is the centre of attraction for many visitors, including hillwalkers.

Eryri is a Welsh-speaking area and its mountains, lakes and valleys are deeply imbued with human as well as geomorphological history. The visitor who is also a landscape lover will do well to note a few of the more common Welsh words as they are often informative about the landscape, as well as evocative of it. For example: *mawr/fawr* means big, bigger, higher, major, greater, while *bach/fach* means small, smaller, lower, minor, lesser (a complication of Welsh is the mutation of letters, especially the first letters of nouns, M, for example, mutates to F; B also mutates to F).

Glyder means a 'pile' of rocks; so Glyder Fawr is the bigger pile of rocks, while Glyder Fach is the very slightly lower pile of rocks. Crib Goch is the red ridge; Moel Cynghorion is the smooth or bald, rounded hill of the counsellors (according to some translations); while in the Carneddau, Pen Llithrig y Wrach is the 'slippery head of the witch'. *Carnedd/Garnedd* and *Y Garn* all mean 'cairn'.

A few useful tips on pronunciation – W and Y are vowels in many words (pronounced respectively, 'oo' and 'uh'); F is pronounced as v; FF as f; OE as oi (e.g. Moel as in English 'coil'); U as 'ee' (e.g. Du as in English 'Dee'); DD as th. Betws y Coed is thus pronounced 'Betoos uh Coid' (rather than 'Betsy Co-ed').

Words common in place names

Aber – (river) mouth or confluence

Afon – river (see also Nant)

Allt – height or bluff, often wooded

Aran – high place

Arddu – dark heights

Bach (and Fach), also bychan, fechan – small, minor, lesser

Ber – hilltop

Beudy – cowshed

Blaen – top, crest, source of river or stream or valley

Bod – home or house

Bont (also Pont) – bridge

Braich – spur or height

Bron – breast (including of hillside) or slope

Brwynog – reedy or rushy place

Bryn (plural bryniau) – hill

Bwlch – col or pass, entrance or gap

Bychan – see Bach

Cae – field

Caer – enclosed pre-historic or Roman site

Canol (also Ganol) – centre, middle

Capel – chapel

Carn, Carnedd (plural: Carneddau), also Garn, Garnedd – cairn, tumulus, mound

Carreg – stone or rock

Castell – castle

Cau – hollow or dip

Cefn – mountain ridge or arm

Ceunant – gorge or ravine

Chwarel – quarry

Clogwyn – cliff or crag

Coch (also Goch) – red

Coed – wood

Copa (also Cop) – summit

Cors (also Gors) – bog or marsh

Craig (also Graig) – rock or crag (so Craigafon – river crags)

Crib, Cribin (also Gribin) – jagged ridge

Croes – cross

Crug – mound

Cwm – two meanings for us: 1) a mountain valley, e.g. Cwm Dudodyn or Cwm Brwynog; 2) a glacial valley or the seat of a glacier (the latter also known in English by the Scots 'corrie' and French 'coire')

Ddu (also Du) – black

Dinas – fortress

Dol – meadow

Drosgyl – rough hill

Drum – high ridge

Drws – door (Drws y Coed – door or gateway to the wood or forest)

Du (also Ddu) – black

Dwr – water

Dyffryn – major valley, wide and flat bottomed

Esgair – shoulder of a mountain

Fach (also Bach, Fechan, Bychan) – small, minor

Faes (also Maes) – field

Fawr (also Mawr) – large, major

Fechan – see Fach

Felin (also Melin) – mill

Ffordd – road

Ffynnon – spring or source (also used as lake name where lake is the source of a river, e.g. Ffynnon Lloer in the Carneddau or Ffynnon y Gwas below Snowdon)

Foel (also Moel) – smooth, rounded or treeless hill

Gaer (also Caer) – enclosed pre-historic or Roman site

Gallt (also Allt) – height or bluff, often wooded

Ganol (also Canol) – centre, middle

Garth – enclosure

Glan – shore or bank (so Glanafon – river bank)

Glas – greenish blue or grey

Glyn – major valley, deep

Goch (also Coch) – red

Graig (also Craig) – rock or crag

Gwaun – marsh, moorland

Gwern – swampy land

Gwyn – white

Gwynt – wind

Haf – summer

Hafod – upland dwelling originally used for summer transhumance

Hen – old

Hir – long or tall

Isaf – lower

Llan – parish or church

Llech – slabby or slaty

Llwybr – path (Llwybr cyhoeddus – public footpath)

Llwyd – grey

Llyn – lake

Maen – large stone (e.g. standing stone)

Maes (also Faes) – field

Mawr (also Fawr) – big, major, greater

Moel (also Foel) – smooth, rounded or treeless hill

Mynydd (plural Mynyddoedd) – mountain

Nant – usually a stream, but sometimes also used as a name for a valley, e.g. Nant Ffrancon and Nant Gwynant

Newydd – new

Ogof – cave

Pant – hollow

Pont (also Bont) – bridge

Pwll – pool

Pen – summit, peak, end

Rhos (also Penrhos) – moor

Rhyd – ford

Twll – hole or chasm

Ty – house (Tyn y Coed – the house in the woods)

Uchaf – upper

Waun – moor

Wen (also Gwyn) – white

Ynys – island

Ystrad – valley floor

Ystum – bend in river

Index of Place Names

Note: all grid references are in National Grid area SH.